CW00406972

LAND DRAINAGE
FROM FIELD TO SEA

Land Drainage

from Field to Sea

by
C.H.J. Clayton

with an original Preface by
The Rt. Hon. Sir Ailwyn Fellows, K.C.V.O., K.B.E.
past president of the Board of Agriculture and Fisheries

and a modern Foreword by
Lord De Ramsey

Logaston Press

LOGASTON PRESS
Little Logaston, Logaston,
Woonton, Almeley, Herefordshire HR3 6QH

First published by *Country Life* 1919
This edition published by Logaston Press 2004

ISBN 1 904396 28 3

Printed in Great Britain by
The Cromwell Press, Trowbridge, Wiltshire

Cover illustration:
Cattle by the River Lugg, 2002, by John Carr

Dedicated to the memory of
Charles Henry James Clayton,
O.B.E., M. Inst. C.E., F.S.E., F.C.S.

'Those who show little respect for the past
are said to be
poor guardians of the future.'

ACKNOWLEDGEMENTS

For help with the publication of this edition of the book I would like to thank Lord de Ramsey; Jill Boulton of Norwich Union; Bruce Gelsthorpe, Riley South and Jennifer Cooke, Partners in Grantham Brundel & Farran; and the Leominster branch of HSBC.

Leonard Chase

FOREWORD

I wonder what Charles Clayton would have made of 'Managed Retreat' known to most lowland farmers as managed defeat. Having drained 300 acres of saltmarsh at Wainfleet, he would have recognised the dilemma and the problems. What he wouldn't have accepted is the failure of our government strategists to think ahead.

Our government has set a target of 70% of organic temperate food to be UK produced by 2010. Perhaps the same ambition should be applied to the production of conventional food, avoiding the unsustainable transport of commodities half way round the world. If it were, the current suggestion that half a million hectares, or one million two hundred and thirty-five thousand acres, of our best soils should be surrendered to managed retreat would strike Clayton as ludicrous, as it does me. Managed retreat is not a cheap option unless, of course, we are going in for unmanaged retreat.

On my desk I have a humble piece of aluminium. On one side there are some Japanese characters and on the other side a number and 'Major De Ramsey'. It is my father's identity tag from Changi, the Second World War prison camp in Singapore, where he starved for three and a half years after capture by the Japanese in 1942. If you were to have said to him and his fellow soldiers, many of whom came from East Anglia, that we no longer need to cosset and care for our most productive soils, he would politely have suggested that you climb back into your spaceship and returned to the planet you came from—and that is before you had told him about climate change. Such a policy is certainly not on the agenda for the rest of the European Union.

It is just common sense to protect our people, our towns and our farms from flooding. I have been a member of drainage boards since the age of nineteen and I quickly learned it is common sense not to neglect the maintenance of our drainage systems. There must be a commitment to sustaining land-use in low-lying areas—it needs to be recognised as an essential component of 'sustainable development'.

It is also common sense for all of us involved in flood defence to be more than aware of the effect our work has on the environment. As a species, how we treat and care for nature governs our own chances of survival. It's in our own self interest. So caring for our water-courses and man-made washland, with thoughtfulness and attention to detail would have received Charles Clayton's full approval.

Lord De Ramsey,
President of the Association of Drainage Authorities
December 2004

PREFACE

THERE are certain truths so obvious that they are apt to be treated as negligible; and the title of this book recalls one, the neglect of which has cost the country a loss that can scarcely be estimated in money. Field Drainage is a topic that has often engaged the attention of agriculturists, scientific as well as practical; but how many of them have stopped to consider that land drainage is of little use unless it extends from the field to the sea?

The problem of land drainage is to remove water from agricultural land where it is not wanted and does harm. Water can only get from one point to another by flowing over an inclined surface. That is a truism which it would be impertinent to repeat, were not the consequences of its being forgotten so painfully evident in England to-day. In certain places, of course, water may have to be lifted, that is, pumped on to the inclined channel; but its ultimate destination is the sea, and it ultimately arrives there by gravitation.

In other words, the drainage of the fields must get into the rivers, and the rivers must take it to the sea. But our rivers are choked with weeds, ingrowing trees, fallen timber, shoals, mudbanks, to name such obstructions as nature places there if she is not checked; apart from the various kinds of obstacles erected by the hand of man. It is hardly too much to say that there is not a river in the country, with the possible exception of the Thames, that is in even a reasonably efficient state as an outlet for the drainage of the agricultural land in its valley. England and Wales are well provided with rivers of every kind. Very few of these are mountain torrents throughout their course—if any such there are, they may be left out of account for this purpose; many which commence among the mountains find their way to the sea through stretches of flat land and lose their impetus of flow long before they reach it. Witness the rivers of the Lake District and of the Welsh Mountains; the Kent, the Douglas, the Dee, the Clwyd, the Conway, the Dysynny, are some of these, whose drainage troubles are well known. The Severn itself floods a large and otherwise fertile plain before it even reaches Shrewsbury.

Those rivers, on the other hand, which should drain the Eastern half of England mostly rise at a comparatively slight elevation, and flow by long meandering courses to the sea. The Thames, the Great Ouse, all the rivers of East Anglia between these two, the Welland and Witham, twin rivers of Lincolnshire, the Trent, all answer to this description. The Yorkshire Ouse again has the characteristics of both classes; by its system of tributaries such as the Derwent, the Wharfe, the Nidd, the Swale, it receives the rainfall of the moors of North-east Yorkshire, as well as that from the far wider and wetter areas of the West Yorkshire Moors, which connect with the Pennine Chain, then flows sluggishly through the Vale of York, and discharges—when the tide will allow—the whole of this vast volume of water through the narrow bottle-neck at Goole.

The statement that none of these rivers are efficient arteries of land drainage is not made in pursuit of any theory of ideal perfection. It is mere fact; and a winter of normal rainfall will show a deplorable picture of willow trunks half under water, of bridge arches hidden by water rising to the keystone on the upstream side, of derelict lock piers, the relics of some forgotten navigation standing like rocky islets in midstream, of broken sluices, of tributary channels and dykes full to the brim with an adverse head of water in the main river and the current setting inwards instead of outwards. On the lower reaches, embankments are all but overtopped and pumping engines stand idle because they cannot lift high enough to discharge into the swollen river. In a winter of heavy rainfall such as that of 1918–1919, the passer-by might see river walls breached, floods swirling over railway lines with a load of uprooted turnips, clamps awash with their precious content of potatoes rotting within.

The reason of this discreditable state of affairs is not far to seek,—it is no one's business to remedy it! Certain portions of some of our rivers are under the control of drainage authorities, but on many of them there is no body with any power to cleanse channels or maintain banks, and not one of them is under the sole control of a single authority for this purpose from source to sea. The Conservators of the River Thames themselves have no power to spend a penny for purposes of drainage, and however admirable is the work that they do on that river for purposes of navigation and hygiene, many of its tributaries (which should serve as arterial drains for large areas) are in as congested a condition as any channels in the Kingdom.

Not that there is any inherent antagonism between navigation, water-power and conservancy on the one hand and drainage on the other, for all these interests are best served by a well-graded and clear channel. It is only where the channel is shoaled and obstructed and where its bed is a switchback of "hills" and hollows that locks and weirs and mills have to steal the water that they cannot come by honestly, and pond it up to make a milling or a navigation head. The absence of any co-ordination of land-drainage authorities is not due to any conflict of various vested interests. Its chief cause lies in the fact that the provision and preservation of cultivable land has not in modern times been regarded as a national necessity.

True, there are drainage authorities in various parts of the country, and many Commissions of Sewers date from mediæval times; they were set up under Plantagenets and Tudors to see that no default was committed in fulfilling liabilities to keep clear "streams calcies goits" and so on or to keep up defences against sea and land water, and their duty is to "tax assess charge distrain and punish" the defaulters. But alas! map-making was no part of mediæval administration, and many of these Commissioners were given areas of jurisdiction so wide and vague that they have gradually shrunk from inanition, so that nowadays you find one body of Commissioners with powers extending (on paper) over a stately-sounding portion of a county, keeping up one short length of seawall and rating a few hundred acres for the cost—another that is supposed to cover a whole county "and the parts adjacent," and has not met as a body within the memory of man, but acts through separate "Courts" wherever there happens to have been a public-spirited series of Commissioners meeting at a particular market town, and does not act at all in less fortunate portions of the county—others again whose conception and exercise of their powers is limited by the practice of an apostolic (or even a hereditary) succession of clerks.

Later there came the period of private enterprise combined with public spirit, and in the times of James I and Charles I, great landlords like Francis, Earl of Bedford, set out to reclaim large tracts of fen land in the Eastern Counties and East Midlands, with the encouragement of the State. Corporations of "adventurers" received charters for the purpose, and, with the aid of Dutch engineers, added to the cultivable land areas like the Bedford Level and Hatfield Chase. But as the Whig principles of politics and economy came to prevail, the elements of public spirit and State encouragement gradually gave place to what was complacently called "enlightened self-interest," and the eighteenth and nineteenth centuries produced a large crop of local Acts setting up drainage boards which consisted of a few landlords or their agents and whose areas of jurisdiction were confined to the estates of those who promoted the Bills. Parliament seems to have exercised little discrimination in the matter beyond seeing that justice was done to any opposing interest by the insertion of protective clauses and so forth. It is thus no uncommon thing to find a drainage authority controlling the middle portion of a river valley with no jurisdiction over its outfall, or empowered to carry out specified works and to do no more than maintain those works, and powerless to extend or improve a system installed say 150 years ago. In 1861, a public Land Drainage Act was passed enabling the Inclosure Commissioners (now the Board of Agriculture) to set up authorities of this kind by Provisional Orders requiring the confirmation of Parliament, in place of the more cumbrous procedure of Private Bills ; but the principle of *laissez-faire* continued in force, and the Department was given no power of initiative.

The result of this historical process is a chaos of authorities and an absence of authority. A single instance of a river draining a great acreage of rich land illustrates the position. The Great Ouse with a catchment area of about 1,750,000 acres, has four or five main channel authorities, half a dozen authorities with power over protective embankments only, and internal drainage boards, bringing the number to nearly a hundred ; even then, only about half the river and about three-fifths of the floodable or waterlogged lands is covered.

The recent campaign for increased food production brought to light the urgent necessity for remedying the defects of the drainage arteries; the Agricultural Executive Committees who were then appointed for each county were compelled by their local knowledge and as a result of the surveys they conducted to report that large acreages were unable to make their proper contribution to the food supply of the country because they were saturated or liable to floods. Powers were obtained under the Defence of the Realm Regulations to carry out works of cleansing and maintenance and to exercise the power of drainage authorities where these made default. The Executive Committee of Norfolk, the West Riding and Cheshire were first in the field, and in many other counties of England and Wales, valuable work of this kind has been carried out in the last two years, so that it may be said that some of the rivers and artificial drainage channels are clearer now than they were in 1916, or for many years before that.

But what has been effected is only a beginning

of the work that is required if full use is to be made of our agricultural land. Mr. Clayton's book shows not only how much needs to be done, but how it can best be done. It states also briefly why such work is necessary, and emphasizes most usefully the fact that land drainage is not merely a means of preventing or carrying off inundation, but that it is necessary in this country to the health of the soil itself. Here we have another of the neglected truths ; even those who do not look upon floods merely as an "Act of God," about which it is useless for man to trouble, or as a profitable refresher for low-lying meadows, are apt to think that the be-all and end-all of a drainage system is to protect land from such floods as may prevent sowing at the right season or may destroy standing crops. It can and ought to do much more than this. The cure of the permanent saturation which poisons so many of our fields is equally important with the prevention of floods. "Grass with reeds and rushes" may be a vision of delight among the dry limestone hills of Palestine, but the sight is too common among the varied soils of our humid island to be attractive to those who desire this country to do and produce its best. In whichever direction you may travel out of London, North, South, East or West, you cannot look out of the carriage window for a quarter of an hour at a time without seeing some meadow growing tussocks of rank grass, clumps of rushes, aquatic mosses, where there should be nothing but fine grasses. The poisoning of the arable lands is perhaps less obvious to the layman, but the farmer knows how much he is hampered in ploughing and sowing and growing his corn and roots by a super-saturated subsoil, and when you find as you may nowadays, the grazing of land in a well-drained area let at £8 to £10 an acre, and land of the same character in a neglected area close by, dear at 30*s*. for the so-called " hay " that can somehow be scraped off it, you realize that land drainage is profitable to the owner, as well as to the occupier.

The Land Drainage Act, 1918, though it was not so heroic a measure as some of its supporters would have wished, removes certain of the obstacles to the formation and combination of authorities whose duty it shall be to carry out this work ; and at any rate recognizes the principle that land drainage is not a purely personal or parochial interest, by giving the Board of Agriculture the power to initiate the necessary administrative changes, and by continuing the power to exercise the functions of defaulting authorities in their stead. It may be that in the future some wider view may be taken of the proper method of managing our rivers, and that each may be administered as a whole, for all the purposes that water can be made to serve—public health, navigation, power, land drainage and all else,—but at least one may hope that the impetus given to land drainage and the livelier appreciation of its necessity aroused by the War will not be allowed to die. This book should help to keep them alive.

AILWYN FELLOWES.

NORWICH, 1919.

CONTENTS

ILLUSTRATIONS

AUTHOR'S NOTE

THE abnormal rainfall of 1912, and particularly that which occurred during August of that year, caused widespread injury to crops and animals all over the country. The highly unsatisfactory condition of many of the great arterial drainage systems then brought prominently into notice gave rise to considerable alarm amongst agriculturists, and urgent requests were made to the Board of Agriculture and Fisheries to investigate the causes of recurrent floods.

Early in the following year the Board appointed a special Departmental Commission, of which Mr. R. F. Grantham, M.Inst.C.E., F.G.S., and Mr. Charles Bidwell, P.P.S.I., were the members, to examine and report upon the conditions in eight of the systems in respect of which the most serious representations had been made.

The Commission, to which it was my privilege to act as Secretary, reported at intervals upon the cases submitted for investigation, and in each case made recommendations embodying the execution of remedial works, most of which had particular reference to the improvement of main channels and their outfalls.

Author's Note

Some of the recommendations would doubtless have been interpreted into action but for the outbreak of war in August, 1914, and the consequent disturbance of financial and industrial conditions.

The subject remained somewhat in abeyance until the enemy submarine campaign and the resulting need of intensified food production redirected attention to the serious need of measures for the prevention or mitigation of flooding and waterlogging of agricultural lands. Nothing was more notable than the insistence of farmers all over the country on the necessity of freeing their lands of surplus water if they were to bring into cultivation anything like the full quota of lands scheduled for corn production.

Regulations which embodied provisions designed to meet the emergency were framed under the Defence of the Realm Regulations, and issued by the Board of Agriculture through the medium of the various Agricultural Executive Committees of the English and Welsh Counties.

It has been part of my official duty to inspect and report upon some 200 cases reported from thirty-two counties, in which it was thought that immediate works which might be carried out under the emergency powers conferred by the Regulations might result in some benefit to the affected lands.

Many of the recommendations embodied in those reports have been carried into effect by Agricultural Executive Committees, and many thousands of acres of land which could not have been otherwise adapted for food production have been sufficiently drained to be cultivated with success, whilst other considerable areas which had previously offered but a hazardous prospect of permanent grazing have been either altogether redeemed or greatly improved as pasture.

Some of the achievements of the Agricultural Committees are recorded at the end of Appendix II.

The experience I was able to gain whilst acting, first, as Secretary to the Special Commission, and later, during the war period, was wide as to range and varied as to kind. Almost every condition of drainage or non-drainage came under notice. Almost every condition of mind amongst the persons chiefly concerned found expression.

As to physical conditions, the basic cause of trouble was and is, undoubtedly, the lack of maintenance of main channels and main outfalls. As to mental attitudes, one has received evidence of every degree, from "Kismet" to high practical enthusiasm. What the representatives of the former would ascribe to the "Visitation of God," the exponents of the latter have brutally attributed to the neglect of man.

These apparently divergent philosophies may not, perhaps, be entirely uncorrelated, but I am bound to say that my own leanings are towards the more mundane view.

The purpose and scope of this book are unambitious. It will probably add little, if anything, to the knowledge of experienced drainage engineers, although it may perhaps serve some purpose as an introduction of the subject to the younger members of the profession and to engineering and agricultural students generally. It has been designed to convey in as popular and untechnical a manner as possible some of the leading principles and items of practice which underlie the operations necessary to prevent the flooding and waterlogging of agricultural land.

My chief hope is that it may assist officers and members of Drainage Boards, Commissions of Sewers, County Drainage Committees, Landowners, Agents and Agriculturists generally, better to understand and appreciate the needs of the systems for the efficiency of which they may be responsible or with which their vital interests may be concerned.

If it should stimulate interest and effort in the direction of Land Drainage, its principal aim will have been abundantly achieved.

Just a word as to the order of arrangement of the book. The sub-title "From Field to Sea" suggests the course naturally followed by drainage water, but I have thought it best to deal with the subject in inverse order with the object of emphasizing the prime necessity of improving and maintaining the main outfall channels. No works for the improvement of drainage conditions either on the lands or in the upper reaches of a river system can yield any satisfaction to the drainage area *as a whole* unless the main channels are in a condition to pass the water away to sea. Such works merely transfer the trouble from a higher to a lower level within the area. Sound drainage engineering must begin at the bottom end of the system, and it is from that end that I have commenced, following the course upward from Sea to Field.

I desire to record with gratitude my indebtedness to my honoured late chief, Sir Ailwyn Fellowes, for the forceful and appealing Preface which he has most kindly written; to the Board of Agriculture and Fisheries for permission to use extracts from the Official Journal of the Board and photographs of the breaches in the embankments of the River Arun; to Professor R. S. Seton, of the University of Leeds, for permission to use photographs of the cleansing operations in the Rivers Foss and Kyle; to Mr. J. C. Evitt Robinson, Chief Executive Officer of the Bedfordshire Agricultural Executive Committee, for permission to use photographs of the improvement works in the River Ivel; and to my esteemed friend Mr. Henry Bain, M.S.E., for his most kind perusal of the draft and his valuable suggestions of amendment and addition.

For historical and other references, I am indebted to the works of Cole and Dugdale; to the Minutes of Evidence of the Lords' Committee on the Conservancy of Rivers (1877); and to the Reports of the Special Commissioners above referred to.

For practical guidance I have leaned heavily and confidently upon the sound knowledge and wisdom, and in a few instances have used the actual words, of Wheeler, than whom there is, surely, no wiser counsellor on the subject of Land Drainage.

DULWICH, 1919. C. H. J. CLAYTON.

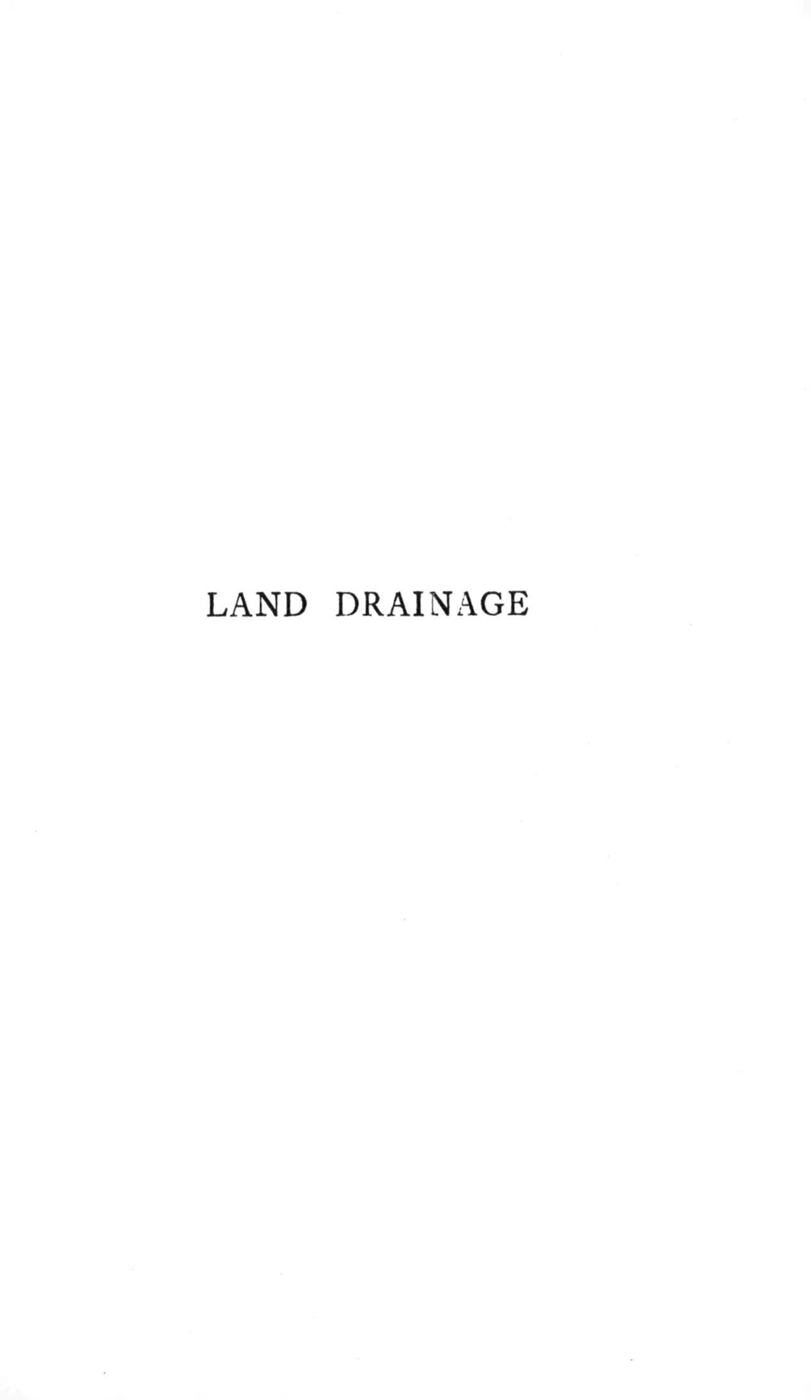

LAND DRAINAGE

CHAPTER I

BRIEF HISTORY OF DRAINAGE LEGISLATION

PROJECTS having for their object the reclamation by drainage of fens and marshes in England appear to have commanded serious attention as early as the latter part of the twelfth century, although the subject was then by no means new.

The first practical effort appears to have been made in 1225, when something in the nature of a Commission of Sewers was set up under a Charter of Henry III. This was "itterated" in 1297 by Edward I; "augmented" in 1352 and 1372 by Edward III; in 1398 by Richard II; in 1399 and 1403 by Henry IV, and "more districtly" augmented in 1473 by Edward IV.

Some time during the reign of Henry VIII, a "settled course of Commission of Sewers" was established with a "verie endlesse power such as hath neither length or breadth against offenders . . . not only against the forenamed inconveniences (acts or neglects) but now for the maintenance and increase of walls ditches banks gutters sewers goates caulices bridges streames and other defenses against inundations. . . ."

Some of the defects of this enactment appear soon

to have become apparent, for an anonymous Essayist (*The Drayner Confirmed or the Obstinate Fen-Man Confuted,* published in 1629 and reprinted in 1647) says: "So bootlesse seemed the labour unto the Counties affected (Norfolk, Suffolk, Cambridge with the Isle of Ely, Huntingdon, Northampton and Lincoln) that the wisdom of the whole Commonwealth thought fit to provide an other Act two yeares after to constraine the Gentlemen of the Countrey under paine and forfeiture to take oath of a Commission of Sewers as they should be thereunto designed."

Questions having later arisen as to finance, a statute was passed in the twenty-ninth year of Elizabeth which provided that, in consideration of certain persons doing certain works of drainage at Earith (Hunts) and Lessness (Kent), they "should have the moyetie of all such gained lands and eighth part of the other moyetie and hold it of the Queene as of the Mannor of East-Green witch is soccage by Fealtie paying a penny an acre and no Tythe for 7 yeares."

In the twenty-second year of the reign of James I, a Session of Sewers was held at which the Bishop of Peterborough, the Earl of Bedford, Sir Francis Fane and twenty-five other knights and gentlemen were present, when a resolution was passed in favour of "giving all lawful ayd and assistance" to the work of drainage of the fens. This resolution was confirmed at other Sessions of Sewers, held in the same year, at Ely, St. Ives, Cambridge and Huntingdon, "where there was 20*s*. set upon every acre for the accomplishment of the work."

A Decree of Sewers which was made at Cambridge on the 20th February, 1622, and reserved by anticipation 120,000 acres of reclaimed land to the King (James I), became inoperative owing to non-fulfilment of the conditions.

The subsequent history of the subject is to a large extent local in its application and interest; its centre of gravity being The Great Level of the Fens called Bedford Level.

Apart from these early schemes of drainage which attracted to themselves the interest "of the whole Commonwealth" as well as the financial support of the early "Adventurers," the subject of the improvement of the land by the maintenance or improvement of the main arterial channels does not appear to have received from the State at any time a conspicuous amount of attention; nor, indeed, has there been such control as might have been expected in regard to many schemes where comparison and correlation would have been advantageous.

Apparently, it has been easy at all times for interested persons or bodies to obtain some kind of local charter to deal with local conditions, more or less after their own fashion, with the result that there have been brought into existence a multiplicity of authorities invested with powers which are often inconsistent with those of similar authorities and sometimes in direct conflict with them. In so far as the State has hitherto appeared to take an interest in the subject, it has rather stimulated than discouraged local and partial treatment as is evidenced by the domestic spirit which pervades all the Drainage Acts down to and including the Act of 1861.

A general review of the past history and present circumstances of many bodies responsible for arterial drainage reveals the fact that, owing either to private rights or to the fragmentary and complex nature of the local acts affecting drainage jurisdiction, the bodies concerned find themselves hampered and obstructed at all points in their endeavour to meet the obvious needs of the river systems with which their functions are connected.

The Select Committee of the House of Lords on the Conservancy of Rivers, 1877, found that: "Owing to the existence of several distinct authorities (and—they might have added—private interests) for the course of a single river, conflicts have arisen which are fatal to the adoption of any uniform scheme of conservancy of the river as a whole, and there is moreover an absence of responsibility which may be held to account in a great measure for the present neglected state of several important streams."

The remedy suggested by the Lords' Committee was that :—

"In order to secure uniformity and completeness of action in dealing with each river, each catchment area should, as a general rule, be placed under a single body of Conservators, who should be responsible for maintaining the river from its source to its outfall in an efficient state."

With regard to tributary streams the Committee considered that :—

"The care of these might, in some instances, be entrusted to district Committees acting under the general direction of the Conservators, but near the point of junction with the principal streams, they should be under the direct management of the conservators of the main channel, who should be a representative body constituted of residents and owners of property within the whole area."

It is probable that since the Report was issued, forty-two years ago, conditions have grown worse, owing to a multiplicity of causes, amongst which are : (*a*) further decay of inland navigation and consequent neglect, by navigation authorities, of locks, sluices, and waterways ; (*b*) further decay of water-milling and consequent neglect of mill-sluices, bye-passes, weirs, spill-waters and tumbling bays ; and (*c*) the increased strain thrown upon channels and banks owing to larger discharges due to under-drainage of agricultural land and by the works of drainage boards and commissions of sewers, of which about seventy, draining some 70,000 acres or so, have been created since 1877.

These would appear to be added reasons for an endeavour to secure "uniformity and completeness of action," but whether the suggested jurisdiction of a conservancy over a whole catchment area, with responsibility for a river from its source to its outfall, is not too large a proposal there may be legitimate doubt.

The jurisdictional area should obviously not extend beyond the lands which might be rated for conservancy purposes, and it is to be recognized that there are, within the catchment basins, very considerable tracts of high lands and mid-lands, upon which, in no circumstances, could flood water lie for an injuriously long period, and which would be unlikely, therefore, to be benefited by works of improvement in the valleys.

The opposition of owners of such lands to being brought within the jurisdiction of a body possessing powers of taxation for drainage purposes has hitherto proved fatal to attempts to give legislative effect to the recommendations of the Lords' Committee.

For somewhat similar reasons, it might not be feasible to frame satisfactory proposals for the administration of the whole length of a river from its source to its outfall.

In the Thames Valley Drainage Act, 1871, it was provided that the limits of jurisdiction of the Commissioners should include "such of the lands in the several parishes townships or places contained in the schedule to this Act as the Commissioners shall from time to time with the consent of the Inclosure Commissioners by order declare to be within their jurisdiction . . . and shall also extend to such part of the river Thames not being under the jurisdiction of the Conservators as is situate . . . (between named points) and also so much of the tributaries of the said river Thames that is to say (naming the tributaries) as flow through or past the several parishes, townships or places mentioned in the said schedule or to those portions of the river Thames not being under the jurisdiction of the Conservators and its tributaries which flow through or past any of the lands which may from time to time, in manner hereby directed, be declared with the consent of the Inclosure Commissioners to be within the jurisdiction of the Commissioners by this Act incorporated."

The limits of jurisdiction in this case were determined by an imaginary line intended to represent a contour taken at a height of 5 feet above the highest marks recorded in the flood of February, 1873, thus limiting the area to that portion of the catchment basin which might reasonably be expected to receive benefit.

In the Somersetshire Drainage Act, 1877, it is provided that the limits of jurisdiction of the Commissioners "shall include such of the lands in the several parishes or places contained in Schedule A . . . as the Commissioners shall from time to time by order declare to be within their jurisdiction whether such lands or any of them shall or shall not be included within the jurisdiction of any body of Commissioners or any drainage board elected under the provisions of any Act of Parliament and shall also extend to such parts of the rivers (named) as flow through or past the several parishes, &c. (in Schedule A) and to those portions of the rivers aforesaid which flow through or past any of the lands which may from time to time in manner hereby directed be declared to be within the jurisdiction of the Commissioners by this Act incorporated."

Defined vertical limits may not have been determined upon in this case, but the scheduled areas certainly do not include upland parishes.

The oft-presented Floods Prevention Bill of the County Councils' Association which sought to make each County Council the chief drainage authority in its own County was doubtless an attempt in the right direction, but it was insufficiently elastic. The boundaries of administrative counties may be quite unsuitable as the boundaries of Rivers Conservancy areas, whether for jurisdictional or for rating purposes, owing to the circumstance that County boundaries often follow the *medium filum* of a river channel.

Some progress has been made towards the achievement of the larger and, if one may presume to say so, the better part of the recommendations of the Lords' Committee and the principal aims of the County Councils' Association by the passage into law of the Land Drainage Act, 1918. This Act invests the Board of Agriculture and Fisheries with powers of initiation, execution and control, and for the first time brings into intimate association practically every interest that is, or might be, concerned with the subject of Land Drainage.

A summary of the Act, taken from Food Production Leaflet No. 56, together with a copy of the Land Drainage Regulations made by the Board under the Act is printed in Appendix II.

CHAPTER II

GENERAL CONSIDERATIONS

THE objects of land drainage are: (*a*) to discharge surplus water from the land so that moist, as distinguished from wet, soil may be left for the healthy penetration and feeding of roots and fibres of plants and for the freer admission of air to the soil; (*b*) to improve the texture of the soil by setting it free to benefit by the contractive and expansive influences of alternations of temperature and by the penetrative activities of earthworms; (*c*) to stimulate by aeration the decomposition and assimilation of mineral and organic substances either in the soil or in the fertilizers applied to the soil, and so to increase the heat-permeability of the soil that it may receive earlier and retain later the "growing" temperatures of summer.

It is well known that ill-drained land is less calculated to take in a store of summer heat than drained land, the summer heat being wasted in evaporating the winter rains and cooling and caking the soil in the process.

If surplus rainfall cannot be carried away either by the subsoil or by means of drains and ditches, it will be likely to accumulate until the level of saturation may be so near the surface as to render cultivation hazardous or hopeless. If, however, the water can pass freely through the soil to a known or prearranged depth, and the surplus be then passed away, the upper soil will be beneficially irrigated, and frost, air and heat will have freer scope as breaking down, sweetening and germinating agents.

In well-drained land, winter rains leave the soil in a moist healthy condition and fit to draw up by capillary attraction whatever moisture may be required during the germinating and growing seasons. Owing to the more open texture of drained soil, its healthy aeration is assured; whilst the resultant encouragement of worm life is of considerable value as a factor of cultivation.

Owing to the more permeable texture of the soil in well-drained land, summer rains are rapidly absorbed; the water is thus conserved against evaporation or surface discharge. During the growing seasons, rootlets are able to traverse the soil in all directions in search of nutriment and moisture, whilst the warmth of the sun, the salts of the earth, and the nitrogen of the air may find free play in a soil which is open to physical and chemical combinations of advantage to plant life. It has been abundantly demonstrated that fertilizing agents are more efficacious on well-drained than on ill-drained land; their nutritive and restorative properties are usefully employed instead of being dissipated in the sodden soil. Smaller quantities, therefore, are needed and better results are obtained for the quantities applied.

Owing to the much wider range from which the roots and root-fibres of plants can draw moisture and nutriment in well-drained land, the latter is far more suitable than badly or un-drained land, to support plant life during periods of drought.

In ill-drained land, the water may lie on or just below the surface for injuriously long periods, so sealing up the interstices of the soil against the admission of air and warmth; drowning out its aerobic life; lowering its temperature and souring it generally.

The broad question which presents itself at the outset of any drainage proposal is, how best to discharge into the sea that part of the rainfall which is not either infiltrated or evaporated. In general, this may be achieved either by the improvement and maintenance of the natural channels, or by the creation of artificial channels into which the water, which might otherwise inundate the land, can be directed either by gravitation or pumping, or both.

Whatever may be the ramifications of a drainage system, there is commonly but one main channel and one outfall: it is necessary, therefore, that these should receive first consideration.

Main outfall channels often run through long stretches of low-lying lands which may be very little above, and are sometimes below, the level of high water of mean tides. In the first case, the improvement and maintenance of the natural channel may be all that is necessary, but in the second case artificial defences must be formed by building training walls or embankments along the sides of the channel.

Whether, however, the main channels are natural or artificial, the gradients through the flatter portions of the lands traversed are necessarily low, and it is owing to this circumstance that one of the most serious problems of arterial drainage arises.

The capacity of a stream to scour its own bed or its liability to silt up are chiefly dependent upon its mean depth and gradient : these govern the velocity of the water. A moderately steep gradient, giving a corresponding velocity, may ensure a channel which is always clean-scoured and fairly permanent in sectional area, whilst one having a low gradient with a correspondingly low velocity favours sedimentation.

Good inclination combined with good depth give the power required to overcome obstacles. A deep stream from its general gravity is a better scouring agent than a shallow stream having the same gradient. The importance, therefore, of the maintenance of a sufficient depth is apparent without distinction of the kind of channel to be dealt with.

There are, however, other factors which in practice complicate the case for the maintenance of channels of streams having low velocities, and one of the chief of these, especially in non-tidal channels, is weeds.

The sedimentation of alluvial ooze upon the bed of a channel is highly favourable to weed-propagation. Once established, the weeds, owing to their screening effect on the silt-laden water, become active sedimentation agents ; once weed-growths have become established, a vicious circle of weeds and silting, silting and weeds, is set up.

In the case of natural channels, whether of high or low mean gradient, there is usually some sinuosity of course, which is, however, much more pronounced in the case of those of low gradient : such streams naturally oppose to the flow of the stream a succession of bends which influence accretion on their convex sides and denudation on their concave sides. Thus, streams which move at low velocities tend constantly to raise their beds and, to a limited extent, increase the sinuosity of their courses.

There is this, however, to be said for sinuous channels of low gradient : viz., that they follow a natural course, and given due and proper attention, they might be presumed to be better adapted to the collection and discharge of the waters of their catchment basins than substituted channels which aim at short cuts across lands whose natural elevation does not permit of their being properly drained into them and whose water may have to be raised by pumping. The natural channels have, moreover, a greater length from the uplands to the outfall than the artificial cuts, and, to that extent, should have a superior value as reservoirs in which flood waters may collect at their natural rate until the surface gradient and depth of water suffice to give the necessary discharge.

Past engineering practice has been to try to obtain outfalls by means of long straight cuts, upon which large sums have been spent, whilst improvements of the main tidal outfall and other natural channels have been more or less neglected.

Whilst it may be conceded that straight cuts of sufficient depth will be far less liable to siltation than old river courses, the latter should not be abandoned in favour of the former without very careful consideration of the possible consequences upon the lands whose natural drainage was towards the river. There is abundance of evidence to show that, in some of the districts distinguished by great artificial channels, the potentialities of the rivers have been forgotten, and that the cuts which were originally designed to serve as aids or supplements have come to be regarded as substitutes.

The ordinary means of maintenance of a main drainage channel fall under three main heads : viz., Roding (weed-cutting), Dredging, and Embanking. It may be said here, that the necessities of dredging and embanking are, as a rule, inversely proportional, but in some cases both are necessary.

Dredging and embanking have to be considered in conjunction, if only because the spoil taken from the channel has to be disposed of and may be needed for embankments. Where it is not so needed, a convenient place of deposit must be found at as little cost as possible. In either case the improvement of the channel by mechanical means can only be effectively achieved by an authority which has adequate control of the banks and forelands, as well as of the channel, throughout the improvable length.

Unfortunately, prevailing administrative conditions often fall lamentably short of this requirement, as may be gathered from the following instances :—

The River Ouse from Earith to the Sea (partly artificial and partly natural) is under five unassociated " River " Authorities, and its banks under nine unassociated " Bank " Authorities.

The Channels of the Rivers Yare, Bure and Waveney are under a single authority ; their banks are under no public authority.

The River Glen, a natural river enclosed between artificial flood banks, is under one authority ; its banks are under three unassociated authorities.

The lower part of the River Welland and its banks are under a single authority. From the Reservoir to Spalding High Bridge the same authority exercises jurisdiction over the river, but the banks are maintainable by riparian owners. From Spalding to Deeping St. James, the Deeping Fen Trust is responsible for the river and one bank, but the opposite bank is the care of two other bodies. This may be a convenient arrangement so far as the section between Spalding and Deeping is concerned as the embankments are flood barriers protecting the areas drained by the respective bodies, but as regards the intermediate section, Spalding to the Reservoir, uniformity of treatment is non-existent and the river is badly choked as a consequence.

The River Trent up to Gainsboro' and the River Wissey are similarly devoid of co-ordination of "River" and "Bank" authorities.

Where there are no "Bank" authorities there may be a liability *ratione tenuræ* which it would be, in many cases, difficult to enforce.

During a recent dredging of the Yare, the River Authority could not deposit the dredgings on the banks where they were greatly needed, having no title to the land nor to the use of it. They had, therefore, to pay contractors to remove, far from the sites of the dredging, the very material that was urgently needed just opposite to those sites for the protection of the lands.

Mr. Wheeler says in his Report to the Denver Sluice Commissioners, dated February, 1884: "The difficulty of properly dealing with this matter (viz., that of banks) is no doubt greater from the separate jurisdiction of the authorities having charge respectively of the river and banks. As the interests are materially the same it would seem reasonable that an amalgamation of these trusts would render the facility for carrying on works of mutual improvement more easy."

Another reason why "River" and "Bank" authorities should be merged is that the grading of the river and its sectional area between the banks could only be properly maintained by one authority.

Irresponsibility for Control

In addition to the control and care of channels and banks, there are other considerations of great importance. It seems clear that the maintenance of channels and banks must depend, to some extent at least, upon the effective control of locks, tidal-gates, outfall and up-stream sluices, and the time when discharges of flood-water should take place.

Unfortunately, there appears to prevail, amongst owners or controllers of such factors, a general condition of irresponsibility to others which is not calculated to promote the happiest relationships. One may find almost everywhere, a complete absence of co-operation to pass flood-water down stream at such times and in such manner as to cause least damage and inconvenience.

The rather haphazarded distribution of embanked lands along an arterial channel is another matter which deserves consideration.

Along the Valley of the Yare there are, e.g., stretches of embanked land, above and below which there may be no embankments worth consideration. The failure on the part of the owners of such lands to provide adequate embankments not only leaves their own lands open to flood-water, but compels the owners of other lands to build lateral embankments against the floodable areas : thus, the total length of embankments (longitudinal and lateral) might suffice, in a given mileage, to protect the whole river frontage, instead of part of that total length being wasted by dividing the lands up into a kind of chessboard pattern of protected and unprotected lands.

The disparity in the letting values of protected and unprotected lands of similar character along a single river valley is sometimes very striking. Excellent pasture or arable on deep rich soils which are capable of feeding full acreages of sheep or stock, or producing high-priced root crops, or market vegetables, may lie side by side with the coarsest of pasture, often foul with rushes and wild iris. Inquiry in one river valley in Somersetshire has elicited the fact that the letting value in the one case was from 90*s.* to 120*s.* (in one instance 140*s.*) per acre and in the other case 15*s.* to 25*s.* per acre, yet it is not too much to say that here, as elsewhere in England and Wales, there is hardly an acre of land that is incapable of being effectually drained, and drained to show a profit on outlay.

Something more than individual effort is required, however. It would be as vain to expect that, say, 500 landowners could build and maintain a main line railway across their lands if each had charge of the length within his own boundaries, as that the same individuals, acting as such, could improve and maintain a fully effective river system either for drainage or any other useful purpose.

CHAPTER III

CATCHMENT AREAS AND THEIR DISCHARGES

THE land surfaces of the earth are roughly divided into a series of irregularly shaped basins, the edges or watershed lines of which are formed by the crests of the hills; and the hollows of which form the catchment areas.

Each catchment area has, at some point, a gap or opening through which the excess water of the area is voidable to sea. There may be within any given catchment area minor depressions which are so nearly landlocked as to have almost no point of discharge, but there are few, if any, lakes without some point of overflow.

Water which falls from the clouds upon a catchment area has three immediate and two ultimate means of dispersal. The immediate means are: (1) infiltration or soakage into the soil; (2) evaporation from the surface into the air; and (3) run-off from the surface into the sea. The ultimate means are evaporation and run-off only, because the reservoir capacity of the soil is limited by physical circumstances which manifest themselves in the form of land springs so soon as the underground reservoirs are full to overflowing.

In summer, a proportion of the water that falls is taken back into the atmosphere almost immediately, but of the water which finds its way through the top soil a very large quantity is absorbed by the roots and fibres of plants and later evaporated through the leaves. A well-grown oak, for example, will absorb and evaporate through its leaves in the course of one season many times its own weight of water.

After the needs of the atmosphere and of vegetation have been met, percolation to the deeper strata proceeds until some level is reached beyond which there must be an overflow. In the case of the permeable solid formations such as Sandstone, Oolite, Chalk, etc., this is termed the permanent water table. In ordinary soils it is called the saturation level. It is with the water which runs off the surface or escapes above saturation level that those concerned with drainage have to deal.

The proportion which discharge bears to rainfall may vary greatly with the general character of the catchment area. For instance, an area which is bounded by granitic rocks and intersected by steep valleys might at once discharge nearly the whole of its rainfall, whilst another area comprising gently undulating or flattish lands of a highly permeable nature might retain or evaporate a very considerable proportion of the total volume.

The volumes of water discharged at flood periods by catchment basins in England vary from a mean depth of about 6 inches in the Midland,

Southern and Eastern districts to about 20 inches in the Northern and Western parts of the country, including Wales, whilst the perennial flow of rivers may be only about 4 inches as an average.

The greater run-off to the Western outfalls is due to the fact that the catchment basins lie generally to the north-west or west of the outcrop of the Lias which extends from Lyme Regis to beyond Scarborough. The affected districts include the Devonian range of the West of England, the Silurian range of Wales, and the Carboniferous range of the North of England. These have more or less impervious surfaces of super-average slope.

On the east of the Lias, the Midland and Eastern County districts are generally more pervious and of moderately gentle slope. The run-off to the eastern outfalls is, therefore, considerably less than to those of the west.

The possible conditions are so variable that, whilst no general rule can be laid down, it is permissible to assume that in average areas in England the discharge to sea is from 50 per cent. to 60 per cent. of the total rainfall. As the general average rainfall is about 32 inches per annum, and as each inch represents an approximate weight of one hundred tons or an approximate volume of 3,600 cubic feet per acre, the water falling upon an acre is 3,200 tons or 115,200 cubic feet, of which, roughly, 1,800 tons or 64,000 cubic feet runs off by rills, brooks, streams and rivers, and ultimately finds its way back into the ocean from which it was originally evaporated.

Catchment Areas and their Discharges

Rainfall records taken in the Fen country continuously since 1829 give the following general results. January to March is the driest quarter; July to September, the wettest. April to September, the wettest half year; August, the wettest month, and February and March, the driest period of the year. Records of wider and more general application indicate that spring is the driest and autumn the wettest season; October is the wettest month; the wettest quarter is made up by October, November and December. The wettest half-year is that between the beginning of October and the end of March. It is clear, therefore, that in providing for the drainage of any given catchment area, the daily average volume over the whole year must be greatly exceeded. Apart from seasonal proportions of rainfall, however, seasonal proportion of run-off to rainfall has to be considered.

The general average result of a very large number of gaugings which have been taken from time to time over a long series of years indicates that about 60 per cent. of the average rainfall is due to the half-year October to March, and that an average of about 60 per cent. of that proportion is discharged to sea. We have, therefore, the general proposition, that of an annual rainfall of 32 inches, about 36 per cent. is run off in 182 days.

The daily average rainfall for the whole year therefore is :—

$$\frac{32 \text{ inches}}{365 \text{ days}} = \cdot 08767 \text{ inch per day.}$$

But during the wettest six months—October to March—the proportion of the total due to the year is :—

ins.

$32 \times \cdot 6 = 19 \cdot 2$ inches, of which

$19 \cdot 2 \times \cdot 6 = 11 \cdot 52$ is run-off to sea in 182 days.

We have, then, an *average wet period run-off to sea* of :—

$$\frac{11 \cdot 52}{182} = \cdot 0633 \text{ inch per day.}$$

In considering the capacity of drainage channels it will be necessary to take into account the occurrence of wide divergencies from the average. Between 1835 and 1843, for example, the mean rainfall for the months June to November inclusive was 61 per cent. of the total, whilst it is notorious that many of the most destructive floods have occurred during the months of July and August. One of the most serious floods of recent years was that of August 25–26, 1912, when nearly 8 inches of rain (about 25 per cent. of the annual average fall) was precipitated in and around the city of Norwich in twenty-four hours and wide damage was caused to crops and animals nearly all over the country.

Whilst it would be impracticable in ordinary cases to make provision for such abnormal conditions as occasionally present themselves, it would be unsafe not to provide drainage capacity for more than the daily average run-off of the wettest period. The degree of allowance to be made has been the subject of much discussion and no little difference of opinion among engineers of great eminence and experience. Drainage schemes have been designed to accommodate run-off volumes varying between $\frac{1}{4}$ to $\frac{1}{3}$ of an inch of rainfall in twenty-four hours due to an annual average fall of 32 inches over very similar catchment areas.

If the discharge from lands were merely that of water which either flows off the surface or filters through the interstices of the soil into the ditches and drains, it might be possible, as a result of a sufficient number of experiments conducted in any given area, to determine for that area a fairly safe run-off figure for the wettest period of the year ; but the unknown factors of future underdrainage, the establishment of pumping machinery or other provisions for the more rapid discharge of excess water, must still be provided against.

It is quite established by experience that surcharged soils discharge their water more rapidly when underdrained, and to that extent hasten flood conditions in the larger channels. There is abundance of evidence to show that flooding in river valleys has been of greater frequency and suddenness since the underdrainage of agricultural lands was begun to be generally undertaken. The reason is that when underdrained land is filled up to a condition of saturation it has two means of discharge : viz., the original surface discharge and the underdrainage discharge. Before drainage, immediate discharge practically ceased as soon as the water went off the surface, for the seepage through the soil into open ditches was very slow. With underdrains in operation, however, the discharge goes on until the pipes, 2, 3 or 4 feet below the surface, have quite emptied the soil above them.

The fact that well-drained land cannot be water-logged serves to show that larger main channels have become necessary since underdrainage became general.

If by underdrainage or other improved means of discharge of land water any given volume due to a catchment area is voided from the soil at more than its natural rate, the natural channels must get gorged in a shorter time and floods must result. Physically, drainage has been usually begun at the wrong end, viz., up-country. Psychologically, it may have been the right end ; for if the more rapid discharge and the more frequent floods have served to direct serious attention to the inadequacies of main channels and their outfalls, they will perhaps have done more good than their designers intended. The late Mr. Bailey Denton called water discharged by underdrains "new" water, arguing that, as before drainage, the water was retained in and later evaporated from the soil, it was now discharged as water instead of being converted into vapour. Estimating the extent of land systematically under-drained in England and Wales up to 1877 at 3⅓ million acres, he deduced that the annual additional run-off due to underdrainage would amount to about 90,000,000,000 cubic feet which would be approximately equivalent to a wet year's discharge of the River Thames.

For the Fen districts with an average rainfall of 24·9 inches, and where underdrainage is perhaps less necessary than in more retentive soils, the late Mr. W. H. Wheeler recommended that the capacity of main drains should be equal to a run-off of ¼ inch of rainfall in twenty-four hours.

As has been previously indicated, absolute safety from occasional flooding due to abnormal rainfall can seldom be provided against, but a good general provision against super-average discharges may be found by multiplying the daily average of the wettest period by 5 and designing the capacities of the drainage channels upon the assumption of the resultant volume.

Adopting this figure for drainage capacity, we should have, for each acre in an average catchment area, $\cdot 0633 \times 5 = \cdot 3165$ inch of water as a basis of the volume to be run-off to sea. This volume is so nearly 1 per cent. of the total annual rainfall —32 inches—that it may be safe to adopt as a general rule that, for an average catchment area in England and Wales, the discharge capacity of main channels should be equal to a daily run-off of 1 per cent. of the annual average rainfall of the district.

This allowance may be regarded by some as unnecessarily high, as the usual allowance for a 32 inch rainfall has been ·25 inch. It is questionable, however, whether any engineer has been at any time called upon or allowed, in this country at least, to provide discharge for the whole of any very large catchment area. Large partial schemes have often been carried out, but technical history seems to point to provision having been made rather for the water that actually came down to the point at which the new works were to commence than for the volume which might have been brought down if the catchment area had been treated as a unit. At any rate, few, if any, of the purely outfall schemes have succeeded in safeguarding lands in the higher portions of the valleys from serious flooding. It is pretty certain that in the past, the full effect of the suddenness of a largely increased flow due to systematic underdrainage has been greatly underestimated. It has to be remembered, too, that there may be a very large degree of soakage through the pervious banks or subsoil of a swollen river on to the flanking lands, and that this water must find temporary accommodation in the drains which would ordinarily have been designed to deal with the land water only.

Another factor which has received too little consideration is that of town and road discharges. There are, of course, within any considerable agricultural area, a number of towns and villages, large and small, besides hard roads, whose total acreage makes up an appreciable percentage of the total area. With modern methods of roofing, paving, sewering and road construction very large volumes of water which would have been otherwise slowly infiltrated or evaporated are discharged, almost on the instant, into the drainage channels. It is probable that 95 per cent. of the total rainfall due to such areas is immediately thrown into the river systems.

The capacity of any drainage system to discharge the required volume of water from any given catchment area obviously depends upon the minimum period of each day during which the outfall channel is free to send the water out to sea.

In the case of a tidal outfall channel, no discharge can take place during the period of flood tide. It is necessary, therefore, to reduce the time-volume-discharge period by the ascertained number of hours in each day which is occupied by two flood tides.

Although, owing to what is termed the "priming" of the tides, the full double oscillation of two floods and two ebbs occupies more than twenty-four hours, it is not necessary to do more than add the two flood periods and subtract the sum from twenty-four hours to ascertain the period of possible discharge.

The ratio between floods and ebbs varies on different parts of the coast and consequently in river channels discharging through the coastline. On the North Lancashire and Westmorland Coasts, the flood tide runs for about 1½ hours and the ebb for about 10½ hours. In the Humber, the periods of flow and ebb are about 2½ and 9½ hours respectively. In the Great Ouse, the periods are roughly as 3½ to 8½, whilst in other tidal channels the periods may vary from 2 to 10 hours in one channel to equality of time in another.

If we take, for example, a case in which the periodicity is as 5 to 7, we should obtain a tide-locked period for the two floods of 10 hours, leaving 14 hours during which the river can discharge its water to sea.

Applying this to a catchment area of half a million acres with a provided wet period daily run-off of ·32 inch we should have a total volume of :—

$$\cdot 32 \times 500{,}000 = 160{,}000 \text{ inches, or}$$

$160{,}000 \times 3{,}600 = 576{,}000{,}000$ cubic feet to be discharged at the rate of :—

$\frac{576{,}000{,}000}{14 \times 60 \times 60} = 11{,}428$, say, 11,430 cubic feet per second.

As no two cases are likely to present equivalent factors, it may be convenient, for the purposes of later discussion, to adopt the figures here assumed and to suppose that the catchment area to be dealt with covers half a million acres and that the required discharge from it is 11,430 cubic feet per second.

CHAPTER IV

OUTFALL CHANNELS

IT may be desirable before discussing the necessary area of an outfall channel to discharge a volume of 11,430 cubic feet per second, to consider the relations between tidal and fluvial waters in that channel.

Tidal water at sea may be taken as representing undiluted sea water. Tidal water in the outfall channel of a river is differently composed, because, although the fluvial water is always flowing downward towards the lowest point possible,—viz., low water mark at sea,—it meets during the period of rising tide an opposing volume of sea water with which it mingles, the combined volumes being operated upon as a unit for tidal purposes, that is to say, the river water which has reached that portion of its outfall channel which is under sea-tidal influence itself becomes tidal and no longer operates under fluvial influence.

Some confusion of idea has sometimes been entertained as to what really happens in regard to fluvial and sea-tidal volumes when they meet, and it has even been suggested that the two volumes should be added together and provision made in the channel for the whole volume which would have come in from sea if there were no river, plus the whole volume which comes down from the river during the period for which provision has to be made.

A moment's consideration will show that, as the flow of the river is perennial, and may be presumed, therefore, to have a minimum depth and width at any given point in the outfall channel, and that as the normal maximum rise of the tide in that channel is not greater than the tidal elevation at sea, the volume of sea-tidal water that flows into the channel can only be so much as suffices to make up the difference between the existing volume of river water and the total volume of fluvial plus tidal water up to the tidal limit.

When the sea tide is quite out, the level of low water at any point in the tidal channel above the limit of low water at sea is the level at which the surface of the river water happens to be. This is sometimes referred to as the low "tidal" limit, but it is clear that tidal water does not begin to count for elevation or depression at that point until flow and ebb have reached that vertical elevation in their upward and downward oscillations.

Suppose the extreme range of the tide at sea to be 20 feet, say 10 feet below and 10 feet above Ordnance Datum, and suppose that at some point up the outfall channel of the river the lowest level reached by river water is 10 feet above Ordnance Datum, that point must be the extreme normal limit of the tide within the channel. As the channel slopes downward towards the sea, the lowest level of the river water at any point below the tidal limit must fall below the level at the limit, and the vertical range of the tide at that point in the channel must be therefore the difference between the local lowest level of river water and 20 feet above low water at sea.

It will be of some interest later to consider the effects of local vertical ranges on local discharges of drainage water into tidal channels, but it may suffice now to take into account, for the purpose of the total discharge of the system, the horizontal distance within the outfall channel between the high-water point at the upper tidal limit and the low-water point at the lower tidal limit.

Suppose this distance to be 20 miles, we have a mean velocity for the ebb of $\frac{20}{7} = 2{\cdot}857$ miles an hour, or $\frac{2{\cdot}857 \times 5280}{60 \times 60} = 4{\cdot}2$ feet per second.

As the required discharge is 11,430 cubic feet per second, the theoretical mean area of the outfall channel must be $\frac{11{,}430}{4{\cdot}2} = 2{,}721$ square feet.

In dealing with natural outfall channels, however, a number and variety of circumstances necessarily have to be taken into account. These may include the occurrence of sinuosities in the course of the channel; the liability of the channel to silt up owing to deposits of detritus from the sea or alluvium brought down by the river, or both; irregularities of cross-section due to "bottle-necking" in the width or shoaling in the depth; sand-bars at the mouth or a tendency of littoral drift to pile up obstructions in or across the estuary and other possibilities, any of which might reduce the capacity of the channel to carry off its water and would dictate a necessity for some addition to the theoretical sectional area. The requirements can, of course, be ascertained only by a complete and thorough investigation of all the local circumstances and tendencies.

The general effect of sudden bends or those of short radius is to encourage accretion on the convex and erosion on the concave sides. The tendency of moving water,—obedient to the general law of motion,—to move in a straight line until influenced by some force outside its line of direction, causes the mass of water to impinge upon the concavities of any bends in the channel, so giving rise to erosion of the bed and banks. The consequence of this action is to deepen the channel in the vicinity of the concave side. Deepening may result in the removal of the necessary support for the banks whose toes and faces are further eroded by the scooping or fretting action of the water which, thrown out of its normal line of direction, grinds its way round the inside of the curve until it reaches some straighter course along which it may resume its interrupted mid-channel course. The local deepening of the channel causes also a local increase of velocity on that side of the stream, but this increase is counterbalanced by a local reduction of velocity on the opposite, or convex side, where, owing to the occurrence of comparatively slack water, any solids held in suspension are almost sure to be deposited.

The general result of the occurrence of bends is to give a local cross-section of bed which slopes from the convex side gradually deepening across the channel to the concave side. This cross-section is joined in the portions of the channel above and below it by the more even and regular sections due to a central stream, the sudden fluctuation from the regular to the irregular and back to the regular sections causing swirls and eddies which may sometimes be seen to drive floats quite across the general direction of the stream or even in an upstream direction until they are caught again by a downstream local current.

Apart from siltation due to bends, very large quantities of solids brought in by the incoming tide may be deposited along the bed of a channel during the short period of quiescence at high tide or during a slow ebb.

The outfall channel of the River Kent, which debouches into the estuary lying between Arnside and Grange-over-Sands, at Morecambe Bay, is constantly shifting its course through the estuary as a consequence of the introduction by each tidal flow of hundreds of tons of sand which, driven far up the estuary during a flow period of only 1½ hours, is rapidly precipitated at the slack water period and is unable to escape again owing to the feeble force of the current during the 10½ hours ebb.

This tendency is said to have been appreciably aggravated by modifications made by the Furness Railway Company in the foundations and piers of the viaduct which crosses the estuary; but however this may be, the rapid siltation of the river channel is a serious matter for the drainage by the river, and even more serious for some of the drainage areas which have artificial outfalls into the estuary.

Very large accumulations of sea detritus are alleged by some observers to have been deposited in the Humber and Lower Ouse channels owing to the action of the rapidly flowing tide in carrying eroded coastal matter up the estuary. Shoals have become islands; islands have been joined to the mainland, and new shoals are constantly being formed. It is said by responsible persons who have devoted much care and attention to a study of the local circumstances, that the great bulk of the detritus is identifiable with the matter which is being so rapidly eroded from the Holderness coast to the south of Whitby, and that the physical composition of the long spit at Barmby-on-the-Marsh which has turned the outfall channel of the River Derwent westward, so that the ebb in the Derwent and the ebb in the Ouse now meet in direct conflict, is almost wholly that of the Jurassic rocks and Boulder clays which characterize the geological features of Holderness.

Whether, in fact, the accumulations are due to sea detritus rather than to warp degraded from the lands drained by the rivers discharging into the Humber, there may be some legitimate doubt. There is little doubt, however, that on balance of degradation and accretion the beds of the Humber and Yorkshire Ouse are being rapidly built up above their original levels, and that an indefinite prolongation of that tendency must in time profoundly affect the discharges of the Trent, Aire, Don, Wharfe and Derwent into the main channel.

One factor which may particularly affect the Trent is that most of the old warping drains which were used to such excellent effect to build up new land in the area of which the Isle of Axholme is the centre, are now out of use, so that some part at least of the great masses of silt which were formerly brought up and deposited over the lands, sometimes to a depth of 2 or 3 feet in a single year, must now be deposited somewhere in the main channels.

The tendencies towards siltation and the amount of deterioration of a channel from such causes can only be determined by experiments carried out under as many and as varying conditions as possible. For example, samples of water taken in specially prepared bottles at the surface, at quarter, half and three-quarters depth ; at quarter, half and three-quarters ebb at each of two points, say 5 miles distant from each other, would afford some means of knowledge of the tendencies. If such experiments were repeated under conditions covering, say, two spring and two neap periods, and it were found that the weight of grains per gallon was consistently higher at the upstream point than at the point 5 miles lower down, it might be fairly deduced that a calculable weight of solids was being periodically deposited between the points at each ebb. Similar experiments on flood tides would show in like manner what proportional volumes of solids were being brought into the channel, and the difference between ebb and flood conditions could be compared for net results.

In the Severn, until 1872, immense quantities of mud used to be brought up as far as Worcester, the tide, which was heavily charged with solids, running for 2 hours at tremendous velocity and ebbing for 10 hours, during which time the mud was so heavily deposited along the bed of the channel as almost to choke it up. Parliamentary powers were obtained in that year by the Severn Navigation Commissioners, and works were carried out to Gloucester with the result that the whole of the deposits were carried away and dredging operation became no longer necessary.

Experiments made some years ago in the Trent showed that the water held solids as under :—

Quarter flood, 299·04 ; Half ebb, 261·87 ; Low water 1,905, and First of flood, 3,150 grains per gallon.

Sand-bars or shifting shoals are a more or less common form of trouble which arises particularly just beyond the reach of the scour of the fluvial and tidal channel. Where the deep stream begins to spread out and shallow into the mouth of an estuary, the scouring force of the water is reduced and dissipated by lateral deflections, and any tendency there may be towards sedimentation is thereby promoted. The effect upon navigation may be troublesome, for the old channels may have to be kept open by dredging. In these cases the interests of navigation and drainage are in some measure correlated. Where, however, there is little or no navigation, conditions may grow so serious as prejudicially to affect the discharge capacity of the outfall channel.

There is at the mouth of Christchurch Harbour, which gives the discharge for the Rivers Avon and Stour, a pebbled beach or rampart of shingle running along the last two miles of the course of the channel on its south-western side. The river, which formerly discharged in a southerly direction, now turns almost due eastward within this bank, which has been formed by the eastward littoral drift aided by the prevalent south-westerly winds. The effect of this deflection of the outfall channel has undoubtedly been to check the velocity of discharge of the two rivers and to encourage siltation in the harbour, not only from the rivers but from the sea, as a good deal of the sand which comes in on the flood tide is trapped by the ridge and deposited over the expanse of the harbour, whence the ebb fails to remove it.

All such risks and tendencies should be carefully

studied and so far as possible guarded against in the determination of the sectional area of an outfall channel. The main object to be achieved is to allow the water as uninterrupted and even a flow as possible. The best course is one long sweeping curve pointing in the direction of the littoral drift, or, if that cannot be obtained, one with curves of very long radius. The gradient of the bed need not be steeply inclined, but the bed should be as low as possible from the upper tidal limit to the greatest reachable depth below low water at sea so as to encourage deep tidal action. If deep water cannot be otherwise reached, training banks should be pushed out towards deep water in order to confine and concentrate between them the scouring force of the fluvial and tidal currents.

The velocity of a stream varies as the square root of its depth ; e.g., velocity is to depth as 2, 3, 4 are to 4, 9, 16, etc. The deeper the stream, the greater therefore will be its scouring effect, or, in other words, its capacity to maintain its own channel against fouling, for not only does a deep stream move with a higher velocity than a shallow stream, but to the increased velocity has to be added the higher grinding effect of mere weight of water on the bed. The difference in velocity of two streams, say, of 9 feet and 16 feet depth will be as 3 is to 4, but the difference in the weight of water moving over those depths will be as 56 is to 100.

The transporting power of a deep stream also is greater owing to its higher velocity and density than that of a shallow stream. A stream moving at one-third of a mile per hour will transport soft clay ; one moving at half a mile per hour will carry sand ; one having a velocity of two-thirds of a mile per hour will hold in suspension fine gravel ; a stream moving at a mile per hour will roll along its bed good-sized rounded pebbles ; whilst one of two miles per hour will sweep along stones as large as tennis balls.

For the reasons above adduced the engineer should endeavour by all possible or convenient means to secure for his outfall the three prime factors of direction, gradient, and depth. As the whole object of land drainage is to get surplus water away to sea in the shortest possible period of time, the aim should be to merge the fluvial and tidal influences with as few and as slight interruptions as thought and skill may devise.

CHAPTER V

TIDAL EMBANKMENTS

THE conditions discussed in the preceding chapter are such as might be found to exist in situations where the lands flanking the outfall channel are sufficiently high above high water mark of ordinary tides to be fairly safe from the risk of tidal flooding. In other situations, however—and these probably form the majority—the channels may flow between depressed marshes or saltings which have been gradually built up by siltation of the estuary and are liable to be overflowed.

The problem of the practicability and economy of reclaiming such lands may reasonably present itself, and it may be at once stated that such reclamations are of immeasurable assistance to drainage. By the provision along the sides of an otherwise unfixed channel of embankments between which the tidal wave must move in an unvarying direction up and down, many of the previously discussed advantages are gained. Depth, weight, velocity and scouring capacity are increased, but against all these advantages there may arise a tendency for any heavy detritus that may be brought in by the sea or down by the river, and which was formerly spread over the marshes, to be deposited within the new channel, generally towards the upper end of the tidal influence where the forces of the tidal and fluvial waters are approximately equal and opposite and where therefore deposition is most likely to take place.

It may be said, however, that, as these possible conditions are curable by dredging, the general balance of advantage is on the side of an embanked channel.

The scope of the subject of reclamation of tidal lands is so large that it is not proposed in any way to deal with it here, nor would it be quite fitting to do so in a work devoted to the subject of Land Drainage. It may be said, however, that those who are interested in the outfall capacity of a river system at the mouth of which reclamation works are proposed to be carried out are entitled in equity to be heard upon the subject of embankments.

For reclamation purposes, the embankments should presumably be placed as near to the tidal channel as is consistent with their stability and maintenance, in order that land may not be wasted. It might also be advantageous for drainage purposes that depth should not be sacrificed to width, but other considerations might dictate the desirability of having the embankments placed at some greater distance back from the natural edge of the channel so as to afford additional reservoir capacity in the form of forelands or washes for the temporary accommodation of extraordinary flood waters.

Another reason why it might be advisable to

leave fairly wide forelands is that the weight of any considerable embankment must give rise to a certain amount of horizontal movement in a riverward direction of the marsh in front of the embankment, and that the stability of the embankments themselves might be otherwise jeopardized and the interests both of the land reclaimers and of those concerned with drainage, prejudiced. Forelands usually collect large masses of river silt, and this may be of extreme value as an additional support to the riverward toe of the embankment.

Embankments designed to shut out water from lands which would be otherwise tidal are nearly always formed of earth dug from the lands in the immediate vicinity or taken from the river channel. In cases where the interests concerned can afford to some extent to disregard the question of cost, or where, happily, there may be plenty of gault or other stiff soil locally available, stiffer soils than those usually found in an estuary may be used with great advantage. Where this can be done, it may often prove to be the cheapest course in the long run, for clay embankments, especially if constructed with puddle-cores with the soil well rammed at each successive stage of building, will stand up to a finer slope or batter than those composed of looser or more friable soils, and may therefore be of appreciably smaller cross-section than the others. Such considerations may be weighed in regard to first cost in the light of haulage to the site of the predetermined mass of earth and the cost of building it up: the longer haul of a smaller mass might possibly balance the shorter haul of a larger mass, in which case the cost of building would be in favour of the smaller mass; but it should be carefully considered, apart from the first cost, how the recurrent charges for maintenance are likely to compare after, 'say ten or twenty years' experience of duty.

Land that is shut in behind a tidal embankment must be effectually drained before it can be economically used for agricultural purposes, and so surely as it is drained it will subside. The rate of subsidence may be so slow as to be almost imperceptible to the residents or workers on the land, but one inch per annum—and this is quite an ordinary or even a moderate rate in reclaimed marshes—will produce effects which may manifest themselves in the movement of embankments as well as in other directions.

It will be appreciated that the soil of an area which has been, up to the time of the building of an embankment, sodden to the surface, has to bear in more or less that condition the superimposed weight of the embankment which may be roughly equal, bulk for bulk, to twice the weight of the water in the soil. If the embankment is of moderately impervious construction, such as well-rammed clay, it will tend to squeeze out some of the water beneath its mass and give it a moderately good bedding; if, however, the mass is composed of alluvium or other permeable soil, some of the water will rise in the embankment by capillary attraction and stay at a certain minimum level above the general surface of the land near the structure. In either case, low drainage of the lands behind the barrier will depress the water level in the land, whilst the subsequent subsidence and consolidation of the soil due to drying will tend to draw the vertical axis of the embankment inward towards the marsh. If the embankment is quite straight, this inward tilting will have no effect upon its length. If, however, the embankment is built on a curved line with the horns towards the river, any inward tilting will tend to lengthen the curve at the expense of the stability of the structure. The convex face, viz., that next the marsh—will be in tension, and the concave face—viz., that next the river—will be in compression.

In a loosely textured embankment, minor fissures so caused may not be easily discoverable, because soil from other portions of the structure may move into them almost as soon as the cracks develop. In punned clay structures, however, the cracks are likely to show themselves pretty evidently, and measures can be taken to fill them up by punning with fresh clay.

The tendency of embankments to tilt inward is naturally increased, and, in the case of outwardly curved structures, very appreciably so, by the pressure of the outside tidal water.

If the pressure were constant, the stressed structure might obtain a permanent set and in a short time accommodate itself safely to its load. Under fluctuating loads due to tidal conditions, however, pressure and relief alternate with each other and a kind of rocking motion is set up which, however little observable it may be except perhaps by the aid of a seismograph, tends towards the loosening of the structure of the embankment. Fissures, perhaps small individually but great in the aggregate, are caused throughout the mass. Water under pressure enters them ; the embankment becomes, at some vulnerable point, surcharged with water which trickles through to the back face, carrying with it particles of soil, and so enlarges the aperture from front to back ; but the tide falls, the trickle stops and the mass settles down to its work of resistance again. Thi sprocess may go on for months or years without serious mishap, and perhaps without causing the slightest concern to those most interested. Some, indeed, hold that it is not a bad thing for an embankment to have a few "safety valves" in it. But let an exceptionally high tide, held up by a stiff gale, attack such a weakened structure and then things happen !

Apart from water, rats, moles and rabbits are among the worst enemies of those whose duty it may be to safeguard the stability of embankments. If not kept down by ruthless warfare, they will honeycomb the structures to the menace of every interest concerned. In a tidal embankment, the burrows are naturally above the ordinary tidal limit on the outer side, but those on the inner side may be well down towards the base. Two such burrows, not necessarily connected, may have between them only a comparatively thin wall of earth, always liable to give way under movements in the mass of the ,structure and in any case a false support to the superincumbent earth which, under unilateral pressure, may slide inward owing to a reduction of basic friction. Or, an unusually high tide may drive water into the outer holes of a series of burrows, and, by imprisoning the air in them, blow up the thin partitions between them and other burrows, so causing a through-break by the water. Once through the mass, the water sets up weir action, cascading down the back slope ; the top of the bank collapses and slides inward, and in an hour or less a rabbit hole has become a tidal gap through which it might be possible to float a battleship.

Experience of recent disasters due to the bursting of tidal embankments in Littlehampton Harbour ; along the Yorkshire Ouse Channel ; in the Don and Aire and Trent Valleys, some of them due to inherent weakness of structure, but others certainly due to the ravages of rodents, has quite convinced the author that too much attention cannot possibly be given to the business of extermination of rodents in or near tidal barriers of earthy construction. With a fairly intimate knowledge of existing conditions over about 180 miles of tidal embankments along the low-lying lands in the Plain of York and in the Trent Valley, one has wondered indeed how long it will be before vermin will have finally restored those fair lands, or some of them, to the sea.

On no account should trees be planted or allowed to grow either on the embankments or on the forelands. There is prevalent a mistaken notion that the roots of trees assist to bind the soil and so to strengthen the embankment. That might be so if the tree were composed solely of root, but it is demonstrably untrue, regard being had to the fact that the roots embedded in the mass form the short arm of a long lever with the surface of the earth as the fulcral point. One has only to see the effects of wind-power in uprooted and overthrown trees far inland to appreciate the fact that to tolerate trees on or in front of sea embankments is to invite disaster. It has been estimated that a tree will hold when in full leaf one-half the pressure due to the area presented to the wind. A tree having a height of 25 feet to the centre of its top growth of 20 feet diameter, with a wind pressure of 10 lbs. to the square foot, therefore would exert a leverage on the earth round the roots of 40,000 foot-pounds, or, say, $1\frac{3}{5}$ horse-power.

There may be, perhaps, no great harm in planting willow sets on the forelands if arrangements can be made that the rods shall be cut down to the crowns annually. Such an arrangement may, indeed, be advantageous, as the roots will help to bind the earth and the short stumps and crowns may assist in breaking up wave action before it can attack the embankment with full force, but on no account should the growth be allowed to reach the stage of "wind-bagging." Better by far that nothing should be grown than that growths should not be cut back at least once a year.

From what has been said of the general tendencies towards deterioration of embankments, it may be appreciated that mere mass is of high value towards maintenance. The thicker the embankment the less likely will it be to rupture from any of the causes which have been mentioned.

Many tidal embankments composed of comparatively loosely textured soil have been built with front and back slopes which afforded too little base in proportion to height. There is a tidal embankment at one spot within the author's knowledge which, having a height of about 11 feet above the "protected" land, has a back slope of about three-quarters horizontal to one vertical with a tidal rise against the outer face to within 10 inches of the top. This embankment was breached twice during 1918, the second inundation covering an immense area and partly submerging an important seaport town.

No smaller batter than 1½ horizontal to 1 vertical can be recommended even for the best composed of tidal barriers; 2 to 1; 3 to 1, or even up to 5 to 1, are not uncommon where cost will permit and prudent engineering allowed to be the arbiter. An embankment having a height of 10 feet, a top width of 4 feet, and front and back slopes each of 2 to 1, would stand on a base of 44 feet. This would probably represent the minimum of safety in a structure of loosely composed soil.

It is usually necessary at some stage, and this

should preferably be the building stage, to reinforce the front slopes of an embankment with brushwood, or chalk or stone or two or three of them in combination. In the cheaper classes of work, thorn fagots, usually termed "kids," made up to a length of 3 or 4 feet and a diameter of about 12 inches and bound tightly with tarred string (marline), are built into the outer face of the embankment, the brush ends of the fagots pointing outwards. The lower tiers should be secured by stakes 6 to 8 feet in length driven down through the fagots at intervals in the line of direction. Willow, thorn, oak or hazel stakes will usually be suitable in situations which may be sometimes wet and sometimes dry. Ash or elm may be used for continually submerged work. The successive tiers of fagots are stepped back so as to conform to the desired slope of the face. The kidding is usually begun at the base of the work and continued upward for a quarter or half or any other required proportion of the height, but it is not usually continued to the top of the structure.

If there is a tendency towards scouring action by the water, the kids prevent erosion and assist in holding up the toe of the embankment which might otherwise be undercut, so causing falls from the face. This kind of reinforcement is found to be very effective at concavities in the course of a channel or where for any reason exceptional erosion is likely to take place. In other situations it may be depended upon to arrest and retain as a valuable facing to the embankment the lighter kinds of solids in suspension in the water.

Chalk pitching of the lower portions of the outward slope with angular lumps 9 to 12 inches across, carefully laid by hand outside the kidded face, affords further valuable protection against erosion. Above this may be built ragstone or slag pitching to a depth of about 12 inches, the outer face of the stone being arranged so as to continue the slope of the chalk. Once properly laid, the pitching will in ordinary circumstances remain *in situ* for a considerable time, but it should be periodically examined for local movement and any loose places keyed up with fresh blocks.

In very exposed situations it may be necessary to stone pitch the whole face and grout the pitching in cement, but one disadvantage of this course is that waves are likely to run up the smoother face and spill over the crest of the embankment to the injury of its back slope.

New embankments should be turfed or sown with grass seed as soon as may be after completion, and the grass should be cut frequently, so as to encourage root propagation. Some engineers prefer that the banks should be left for a time, say twelve months, to consolidate, before being sown. This may be an economy in grass seed, as the first crop may have to be covered up by fresh earth added to restore the original height and slopes, but if no great additions of earth are necessary, the first sown grass, once firmly rooted, will find its way through the new topping without abandoning the greater depth of its first rooting. For this reason the reinforced skin of the bank will be permanently thicker than it might otherwise have been.

Subsided embankments should not be repaired by mere " cradging " or " topping." If the whole structure were found after consolidation and subsidence to be, say, 1 foot lower than the original height, and a foot of earth were added to its top face only, the slopes of the added earth being in line with the slopes of the mass, the new top width would be less than the original top width, and successive operations of that kind would finally bring the top to a knife edge marking the line of intersection of the front and back slopes. The original top width should always be maintained, and to this end whenever the original height is restored, so also should be the original thickness and slopes.

All embankments of 6 feet or more in height should be protected against accumulations of water in them by soak dykes, which should be cut at some little distance from and parallel with the toe of the back slope. They may be of relatively small sectional area, say 18 inches in width and depth for embankments up to 7 or 8 feet in height, and they may be formed at any convenient distance up to say 16 feet from the toe, but not near enough to deprive the embankment of support. Their effect is to arrest and carry off land water which might otherwise find its way into the footings of the embankment and to drain the structure of any water which might otherwise saturate its mass.

CHAPTER VI

LIMITATION OF TIDAL FLOW

BEFORE leaving the subject of tidal channels, it may be desirable to make a brief reference to the vexed question of barrages or sluices intended to limit the length over which flow and ebb would naturally operate, so as to form non-tidal flood water reservoirs behind them.

There are numerous instances of sluices having been built across tidal channels, but in each instance within the author's knowledge the immediate or contingent purpose was rather in the interests of navigation than of drainage.

When a tidal channel gives entrance to a navigation system, it may be vital to the success of the navigation to retain a good head of water in the river after the tide has receded, and the usual way to achieve that end is to prevent the water from escaping on the ebb by placing across the channel a barrier in the form of locks through which vessels may pass up and down without voiding more than a lockful of water at each operation. In some cases weirs also are provided, but in any large navigation system which does not lend itself to the voidance of excess water by weirs alone, it is necessary to provide drainage eyes or sluices which can be drawn whenever the volume behind the barrier is greater than can be otherwise conveniently passed away.

From the point of view of excluding tidal water which would otherwise reach a vertical height incommensurate with low embankments in the upper part of the channel, something may be said for a purely drainage barrage or sluice placed across a tideway. It would operate as the high end of a high-sided trough behind which the embankments could be kept at a less height than might be otherwise required to prevent tidal overflow.

As regards storage, it is arguable that one might expect to gain as much storage capacity behind a cross-tidal barrage as is represented by the enclosed length multiplied by its mean width multiplied by the difference in height between the mean level of the river water and the mean high tide. This view, however, seems to lose sight of the volume of river water which would, if there were no barrage, continue to pass down channel whilst the tide was rising over the length cut off by the barrage. As previously explained, the outflowing river water mingles with the incoming sea, or, owing to its lower specific gravity, flows on top of it, but in any case, ultimately becomes tidal. If, therefore, the flow of the river is stopped at a given point, the tidal volume which was formerly made up of outflowing river water plus inflowing sea water is made up of less river water and more sea water than its former composition, and the reservoir capacity for river water above the barrage is reduced by the volume of the difference. In this case, the vertical dimension for storage can only be the difference between the ultimate levels of the tidal and river waters in front of and behind the barrage, respectively.

The rising tide is itself a barrage, but of course a moving one. It pushes back some of the river water in the tidal length, and to that extent the energy of the tidal wave is curtailed ; but from the moment when ebb conditions come into play there is more than a complete recovery, for the tidal reflux is then stimulated by the energy of the fluvial water behind it, and the double influence comes into operation as a natural and powerful scouring agent. Whether it is wise, therefore, from the purely drainage point of view, to limit the traverse of the tidal barrage is rather questionable. Navigation requirements are another matter altogether.

It is open to question whether the tendency towards siltation both above and below a fixed barrier might not outweigh any of its supposed advantages. The effect of an artificial barrier is that the swing or sweep of the tidal wave is artificially arrested, and what was a regular rhythmical oscillation up and down channel is stopped at some point short of the full swing of the tidal wave. As a consequence, abrupt reflex action at that point is set up, and the solids which might have remained in suspension whilst the stream held its course are to a large extent thrown down.

Limitation of Tidal Flow

It has been argued that any excess of siltation either in front of or behind a sluiced barrage can be prevented or cured by judicious sluicing action: i.e., by retaining a good head of water behind the sluice until after the tidal head has become appreciably reduced and then letting it out with a rush. The question seems to remain, however, over what proportion of the length of the channel above and below the sluice can its scouring action operate?

Water which passes over a fixed cill to a lower level takes the superficial form of a parabola which gradually flattens out on the upstream side to an inclined plane. In the immediate neighbourhood of and for some distance behind the sluice, the silt is doubtless caught into the influence of the cataract and swept through the opening, but it is doubtful whether deposited silt a mile or two behind the cataract is more than very slightly disturbed.

The weir action immediately below the sluice has a digging effect, and probably scoops out any temporarily deposited silt in its vicinity and for some distance down channel; but water will only transport as much solid matter as its volume and velocity permit, and any accession of locally scoured or dug up material from above or below the sluice may easily prove too great a burden for it, in which case the solids will gradually settle down at points below the immediate influence of the sluice.

It seems fairly obvious, too, that the scouring effect of the tidal swing must be diminished over considerable lengths of the channel by the interposition at any point of a cross-tidal barrier. The flow is stopped and the ebb starts at an unnatural limit. The grinding effect of a given weight of water moving over the bed of the channel at a given velocity for a given period of time is curtailed, and the effectiveness of the work which was being performed must be as surely reduced as would be that of a file which was suddenly arrested at half-stroke.

There are, of course, hundreds of cases of barrages or sluices across the outfall ends of rivers or artificial drainage channels which discharge into tideways, but in nearly, if not all instances the object has been less of securing reservoir capacity behind the sluices than of saving the cost of construction and maintenance of perhaps scores of miles of embankments, and of enabling low-level cuts and pipe drains to discharge into low-level mains without the risk of tidal influx. The sluices are usually placed as near to the main tidal channel as possible, sometimes within the alignment of the tidal embankment, so that, apart from any other advantage, there is only a short steep apron below the cill of the sluice, and it is thus an easy matter to flush off any accumulation of silt that may gather outside the doors during the tidelocked period.

Without prejudicing the question of the advantages which might accrue to drainage, or the damage which might result to drainage, from the construction of a cross-tidal storage barrage in any particular channel, one may be permitted to point out that the primary business of the drainage engineer is to get the largest volume of surplus land water away to sea in the shortest period. If by a temporary storage of land water during tidal flow the net time-volume-discharge capacity of the river is increased, a sluiced-barrage may be and should be a very good thing. If nothing is gained, it must be a useless expense. If something is lost, it can be only a nuisance.

The balance of professional opinion as expressed in the Reports of various expert Inquiries and Commissions, in this country, in Holland, in France and in Germany, appears to be that any influence that may interfere with the free flow of tidal water up and down a river channel cannot but be injurious to that channel, and that any form of obstruction is certain to give rise to the formation of shoals. [1]

[1] Summarized from W. H. Wheeler's *Tidal Rivers* (Longmans).

CHAPTER VII

NON-TIDAL ARTERIES

ABOVE tidal limits, the principal causes which militate against efficient arterial drainage in what may be termed " open " systems are insufficient or irregular sectional area; insufficient or irregular gradient; insufficient depth; ingrowing trees and bushes and the presence of weeds. In other than " open " systems, locks, sluices, mills, weirs, dams or other structures across the channel may be mentioned as impediments to full discharge.

In an " open " system, we find a certain number of watercourses each of which approximates to an inclined plane or a series of inclined planes. These may differ from each other very considerably; those coming immediately from the high lands being steep, shallow and narrow; those flowing through the levels having flattish gradients and much greater depth and width. Intermediate between these extremes are the main tributaries having high gradients and small sections at the upper ends, but gradually flattening and widening as they approach the parent river, each of them receiving *en route* the waters of minor streams, brooks, field ditches and drains, all of which help to throw added duties upon the main channel by which the whole run-off of the system has to be carried down to the sea.

If all the lands whose waters discharge into an arterial channel were inclined inwards towards that channel or its tributaries, drainage problems would be of simple solution; but it is seldom found that land-slopes are quite so kindly for any considerable length of a river valley. Nature usually arranges her river valleys as a succession of steeps and flats. It is particularly with the latter that the drainage engineer has concern, for his primary duty is to arrange that his system shall be as far as possible adequate to the discharge of excess water from the lowest land in the valley.

Let it be assumed for the moment that the whole of the lands in the valley can be effectually drained by some means—and this is generally true—we have to discharge from our supposed catchment area of half a million acres an assumed volume equal to five times the wettest daily average, or 576,000,000 cubic feet, in twenty-four hours.

In discussing the area of the tidal outfall channel, the time factor became reduced to fourteen hours as the period represented by ebb conditions. In the case of the non-tidal channel, however, the run-off will be constant. We require, therefore, a main channel which will be capable of voiding its water at the rate of $\frac{576,000,000}{24 \times 60 \times 60} = 6,666$ cubic feet per second.

Suppose it to be ascertained that the mean velocity of the main stream between the upper end of the outfall channel and the nearest of the main tributaries is 2·5 feet per second, the theoretical mean area of that part of the channel must be $\frac{6666}{2 \cdot 5} = 2{,}666$ square feet, or about 55 square feet less than the theoretical mean area of the outfall channel which was assumed to void the water during fourteen hours at a mean velocity of 4·2 feet per second.

Having arrived at the theoretical size of the channel for the total discharge from the catchment area into the tidal outfall channel, it becomes necessary to ascertain the capacities of the main feeders to discharge their quota into the main artery.

Now, each tributary stream is the main artery of a catchment area of its own, and although we know the total area and run-off of the mother catchment area, it is necessary to ascertain how much of the grand total is due to each subsidiary area. This information can be obtained with substantial accuracy by dividing the mother area into its component parts by tracing out on a one-inch scale, hill-shaded Ordnance map the watershed lines within the larger area. After marking the boundaries of each of the smaller areas, one for each tributary discharging into the main artery, it will be easy to compute the respective areas for a comparison of each with the total.

Suppose there are nine tributaries, each having

its own gathering ground, and that a computation of their areas shows the proportions to be 9, 8, 7, 6, 5, 4, 3, 2, 1, making a total of 45. We may proceed to number the tributaries in the order of their volumes and then consider their respective requirements for discharge. Tributary No. 9 contributes $\frac{9}{45}$ of 6,666 cubic feet per second; tributary No. 1, $\frac{1}{45}$; and so on through the series. If the rates of discharge were all equal, it would be perfectly simple to ascertain by calculation the necessary sectional area for each length of the main artery and for the discharging portion of each tributary.

The main artery, up to the mouth of the tributary nearest the mouth of the river, would have its full 2,666 square feet. If that were tributary No. 9, the area might then diminish by $\frac{9}{45}$ up to the next tributary, and so on in an upstream direction. But as the mean velocity of each tributary is likely to differ from that of any other or of the main artery, it would be necessary to find out for each at what rate its water comes down.

If, say, Nos. 5 and 6 discharged close together from opposite sides of a narrow portion of the valley with high hills as their main gathering grounds, their mean velocities might be many times greater than that of the artery near their confluence with it. Their water would be rapidly discharged into a comparatively sluggish stream, and local flooding would inevitably result unless the main channel were in some way adapted to accommodate the sudden influx. The theoretical area might be insufficient at that particular point, and some increased reservoir capacity would have to be added to prevent the overflow of banks until the stress was over.

Not only would extra accommodation have to be found for the waters of Nos. 5 and 6, but as their rapid contribution of water might tax the provided reservoir to its full capacity for a time, the water coming down channel from the higher tributaries would be "backed up," so that, owing to causes to which their inherent conditions might have in no wise contributed, the upper portions of the main river and its upper tributaries might overflow or burst their banks unless they also had been provided against spate conditions in their lower reaches.

Conditions vary so widely that it would be vain to do more than indicate the nature of the factors which may have to be taken into account in providing for each part of a river system such a capacity as may in ordinarily recurring circumstances suffice for the general and particular needs. Each factor must be carefully weighed, not as a unit but as an item of the unit problem how best to carry off the excess water of the system so as to prevent flooding or waterlogging of the lands.

It may be desirable to point out here, that the required mean area of a channel varies in relation to what is known as its hydraulic mean radius. The best section, that is the shape which would give the largest mean radius and therefore the largest discharge for any given gradient, is a semicircle in which, of course, the depth is half the width. This shape is usually unobtainable in rivers, or indeed in earth channels of any kind; but in this or any other form, the hydraulic mean radius is obtained by dividing the length of the wetted perimeter into the total area. In the case of a semicircle of, say, 20 feet radius, the perimeter would be $3{\cdot}1416 \times 20 = 62{\cdot}832$ feet and the area 628·32 square feet. Then $\frac{628{\cdot}32}{62{\cdot}832} = 10$, which represents the hydraulic mean radius of the channel when running full.

If the hydraulic mean radius and the gradient are known, the theoretical discharging capacity of a stream can be determined by the formula:

$$V = \sqrt{R \times 2F}$$

where V is mean velocity in feet per second; R, hydraulic mean radius in feet; and F, fall in feet per mile. Assuming that it were possible to obtain a hydraulic mean radius of 10, and that the gradient averaged 4 feet per mile, we should obtain:

$$V = \sqrt{10 \times 8} = \text{say, 9 feet per second.}$$

If, as is far more likely to be the case in an earthen channel, the depth were from one-fourth to one-tenth the width, the wetted perimeter would bear a higher ratio to the area than in the semicircle, and the division would therefore yield a hydraulic mean radius of lower value. Thus in a channel having the same sectional area as the semicircle (628·32 square feet), but made up by a mean width of 60 feet and a mean depth of 10·47 feet, we should have a hydraulic mean radius of $\frac{628{\cdot}32}{80{\cdot}94} = 7{\cdot}75$, which at the same average gradient would give a velocity of 7·87 feet per second, or, say, $1\frac{1}{8}$ foot per second less than that of the perfectly shaped channel. In large channels, V may be taken at 90 per cent. of its calculated value, but in small channels a deduction varying from 20 per cent. to 40 per cent. should be made for friction of sides and bottom of the channel.

In determining areas, therefore, strict regard should be paid to the possible shape of the channel. Although it may be impracticable to obtain the perfect shape, the nearest approximation to it should be aimed at. The more nearly the depth approaches to one-half the width, the smaller will the area need to be for a given discharge at a given gradient.

As in tidal channels, so also in non-tidal channels allowances must be made for deterioration and the consequent reduction of discharge capacity. Accidental and seasonal causes usually operate with more damaging effect to up-country than to tidal channels, and for that reason a generous allowance should be added to an otherwise accurately ascertained area for any required discharge.

If the channel were quite straight; running between well-shaped banks of gault or clay or chalk; unfringed by trees or bushes; not used by cattle for drinking or sheltering, and otherwise very favourably conditioned, the only allowance needed might be that for summer weeds. If, however, the channel ran through "light" land; were sinuous and therefore liable to shoaling at the convexities and scouring at the concavities with a consequent tendency towards the undercutting and slipping of banks ; if, as a further consequence of irregularity of course and section it were liable to rapid siltation and the concomitant propagation of weed growths ; if it were liable to receive large quantities of falling leaves during the autumn, or to become constricted by ingrowths of trees or bushes, or if the sides were liable to be trodden in by cattle ; if, in short, the channel were of the average English character, a fairly liberal allowance would have to be made for deterioration.

CHAPTER VIII

IMPROVEMENT WORKS

IN arranging for the improvement of a defective course or an inadequate cross-section, it may be of considerable importance to provide that the normal maximum water level in the improved channel shall be below the outfall ends of any pipe drains. Large sums of money have been expended from time to time in the under-drainage of agricultural lands with the object of freeing them from a liability to waterlogging, whilst in too many instances the money and effort have been wasted owing to the subsequent super-elevation of the water level in the streams due to neglect of their channels.

It is to be remembered that when the outfall ends of pipe drains are submerged, the drains not only fail to act properly, but that river water enters them and passes up by what then become irrigation channels into the very lands which were sought to be drained.

Other circumstances permitting, an increase of the depth of the bed of the channel is the first and best course to adopt ; but circumspection must be used, as too great an increase of depth may easily defeat the object in view. If, for example, the nature of the soil which composes the channel were of very loose texture, such as sand or sandy loam, it might be very risky to excavate or dredge the bed to any appreciable extent without at the same time cutting back the banks to such a slope as might be otherwise unnecessary.

The bed of a channel is the natural base upon which the sides rest. If that base be of such a nature that it will not bear having part removed without jeopardy to the support of the sides, very little deepening can be done. If, however, deepening and widening form part of one operation for improvement, depth should be kept as low as possible consistently with the safety of the banks.

It is in any case necessary, when arranging for the lowering of the normal water level in a river channel, to pay some regard to the fact that the banks will lose part of the support which the horizontal thrust of the water gave them. A reservoir composed of moderately loose soil with sides nearly sheer might very well maintain its shape owing to uniform and constant pressure, but if the water were drained away the sides would probably collapse inward owing to the removal of the pressure which had held them up. Similar collapses may occur in the sides of a river channel in which the water level is reduced, but in the case of the channel there is the added danger that, as the velocity of the stream is increased by added depth, undercutting of the banks at or below the reduced surface level may take place.

It is better in most cases to arrange that deepening and widening shall be carried out as a single operation, and that the sides of the channel shall be sloped back from the improved bed level to as great an inclination or " batter " as the circumstances dictate. In stiff earth, batters of 1½ to 1 and 2 to 1 are not unusual. In loose soils as much as 5 to 1 may be necessary. The greater the batter the more secure will be the banks and the larger the reservoir provision for flood waters.

The re-gradation of the bed of a natural channel to its natural inclination is seldom possible in practice. The inverts of bridges or culverts may be too high, or other factors may be present which would prevent the formation of an even gradient from end to end of the length to be improved. Where there are immovable physical ordinates such as bridge inverts, the gradation of the bed should be as far as possible arranged so as to be even and continuous over the section of channel between each such point and the point next above or below it.

Between structural ordinates, grading should preferably begin and end at a somewhat lower level than the depth of the structure, but with due regard, of course, to the continued security of the structure. In specifying for work of the kind it has been the author's practice (in suitable cases) to provide that " the bed shall be lowered to a level of say 6 inches (9 inches or 12 inches) below and on the —— side of the invert of bridge 'A' and be graded from that level at an even inclination to a level of 6 inches (9 inches or 12 inches) below and on the —— side of the invert of bridge 'B.'" The reason for this provision is that, although the water below the levels of the inverts cannot get away and therefore that the deeper bed adds nothing to the effective area of the channel, the frictional resistance of an earthen bed is eliminated and a bed of water substituted. As the frictional resistance of the sides and bed may consume as much as 40 per cent. of the discharging capacity of a small river channel, the introduction of a film of water between the hard bed and the running stream is of real value. Another advantage of the added depth is that weeds must grow to a height equal to the greater depth before they can begin to operate as impediments to the flow of the stream.

Depressed sections act usefully also as silt traps. They localize deposits which might be otherwise precipitated all over the channel, whence it would be more difficult and expensive to remove them.

The provision of open-ended flood water reservoirs or "washes" is sometimes desirable as an alternative or a supplement to other means of improvement, but these can only be arranged by building embankments alongside the course of the channel or, in the case of a sinuous course, in moderately straight and parallel lines between which the sinuosities of the natural channel may wander. The provision of embanked washes may occasionally offer a valuable alternative to straightening a winding channel. Little land is lost, as the washes can be grazed by cattle and sheep during the greater part of the year.

Vermuyden provided between the Old and New Bedford Rivers, washes containing an area of 4,765 acres. Until the early part of last century, they served to accommodate all flood waters coming down the Ouse past Earith, being bounded on the south-east by the inner bank of the Hundred Foot River and on the north-west by the outer bank of the Old Bedford River, each about 21 miles in length. In 1812, however, the owners and occupiers of the washlands, finding it inconvenient that their lands should continue to serve as a receptacle for surplus water from above Earith, obtained Parliamentary powers authorizing them to erect a bank 4 feet 6 inches higher than the level of the washes and to erect a sluice, known as the Seven Holes Sluice, at the upper end of the Old Bedford River. As a consequence of these works, any but extraordinary flood water must now go elsewhere than over the washes, as the Seven Holes Sluice is not drawn until flood levels reach a summer height of 4 feet 6 inches or a winter height of 2 feet 6 inches above the washland level. Is it too much to hope that these washes will one day be made available again as a reservoir for Ouse flood waters?

The cost of improvement of a river channel may vary considerably, according to the methods adopted. In the case of narrow channels, where also there is no great depth of water, hand labour may be best and cheapest. In such cases the channel may be conveniently dammed off in sections, the water being bye-passed to one side or other of the dams as the work proceeds. With larger and deeper channels, it may be more advantageous to use scoops and rakes worked by hand or windlass from the banks. In still larger channels river scoops operated by steam power may be most economical. The usual method of working the scoops is to have either two traction engines, one on each side of the channel, or one traction engine on one side and land anchors on the other side. The scoop is first passed backward across the channel by means of a wire rope passing over the drum of the engine on the far bank and is then drawn forward by another rope winding on to the drum of the near engine, the material is collected as the scoop comes forward and is deposited on the bank as an attachment to the lower lip of the scoop is released so allowing the scoop to capsize.

The scoop, which usually has a plain bottom edge for cutting into mud deposits, may be fitted with a tined blade something like a very coarse saw, for the readier removal of weed roots. The scoop is perforated so that it drains itself as it comes up the bank. A possible difficulty with such an appliance is that hedges or other obstructions along the banks of the channel may interfere with its free transverse action. The most favourable situations are where open lands immediately flank the channel.

In larger channels it may be best and cheapest

to use a dredger. Bucket or ladder dredgers, although very efficient tools, can only be used from floating barges or pontoons, and they have the disadvantages that they cannot work at largely varying depths and that, unless they are fitted with conveyors, the spoil cannot be easily disposed of as it is brought up but must be deposited in the vessels for later removal and deposit. If, as is probable, the spoil from the bed is needed on the banks, the expense of local dumping and later cartage of the material is added to that of the actual dredging.

Grab dredgers to lift from ¾ to 1 cubic yard are often found to be the most useful and inexpensive all-round tools for heavy work. They can be worked either from the banks or from any convenient form of floating vessel, and the positions can usually be so arranged that the grab can immediately deposit the spoil where it is needed. One great advantage is that they can bring up spoil from any reasonable depth. Another is that they tear out and bring up the roots of weeds.

For really large channels grab dredgers do their work very economically. One particular machine, which has a jib radius of 45 feet and can deposit the spoil on a bank 30 feet from the side of the vessel and 17 feet above flotation line, has recently removed 138,000 cubic yards of mud from a large drain in Norfolk at an average cost of a little over 4*d*. per yard. A ¾ yard grab dredger has been used very successfully during the past ten years in maintaining the channels of the Vernatts and Counter

Drains in the Deeping Fen system and in the rivers Glen and Welland. The cost of the work has averaged about 4*d*. per cubic yard, including the repair and maintenance of the dredger.

For soft mud or sand, suction dredging may be best and cheapest, but the general clearance and improvement of an average river bed may need much heavier and rougher work than a suction dredger alone could tackle.

A word of warning may be uttered here against dredging of an indiscriminate character. If, for example, the channel of the river to be improved runs through a deep oolite, or gravel, or other highly porous formation, it is at least probable that the entire removal of whatever waterproofing agents may have collected on the bed as a result of years of natural siltation would be followed by startling results. The Churn, for instance, rises in seven wells in the Cotswolds. Gaugings have shown that at its source it discharged 31 cubic feet per minute. but went on accumulating as it passed over clays and other retentive soils until at 5¼ miles below its source it discharged 320 cubic feet per minute. After traversing a length of inferior oolite the volume gradually diminished. At 6½ miles the flow had fallen to 290 cubic feet per minute; at 8⅓ to 113 cubic feet per minute; and at Cirencester it was only 30 cubic feet per minute. Some years ago a Committee of owners along the Churn was formed for the purpose of safeguarding the water, and as a result men were employed to puddle the bed with clay and stop up cracks by a process known as "wracking."

The Frome, another case of the kind, rises in the Chalford Springs which emerge from the base of the oolite from Liassic Sands. After flowing for 7 miles it becomes almost dry during summer time, and at the best of times loses half its water to earth.

The River Misbourne flows between Amersham and Denham over deep beds of gravel, and it is stated that injudicious clearances of the bed have occasionally resulted in loss of water. The fact that water from a river may be lost into the subsoil has been sometimes taken advantage of for drainage purposes. The late Mr. Bailey Denton successfully treated a flooded area on Lord Dillon's estate in Oxfordshire by sinking a sump 20 to 30 feet deep into the oolite. The land became entirely free of water.

Although no very large experiment of the kind has been so far carried out in this country, there would seem to be no reason why, where geological conditions are favourable, part at least of the flood waters of a catchment area should not be sent to earth. Where the area overlay, for example, New Red Sandstone, Oolite or Bagshot sand, the amount of soakage should be very considerable.

Neither trees nor bushes should be allowed to grow on or close to the banks of river channels. If they are there already, they should be cut down to bank level and removed to a place of safety. The natural tendency of any tree growing near the water's edge, as elsewhere, is to lean towards the side of least resistance. From having at first a picturesque tilt it may in the course of years get to lean at such a dangerous angle that a high wind may lay it across the stream, where, if left undisturbed, it will usually re-root itself in the bed. Until quite recently the River Swale, which runs through a loose sandy formation, was so full of fallen trees, many of them flourishing on islands they had collected from the silt, that at flood times one was able to see in the length between Kirby Wiske and Myton scores of veritable cataracts over these accidental obstructions. In the Derwent, too, one has seen a tree over 25 feet in height growing quite in the fairway into which it had slipped bodily and upright with a mass of the bank about its roots. The River Bollin from Warburton to its outfall into the Manchester Ship Canal is so choked with fallen trees that flood waters rise at Warburton Bridge at a terrific rate. It is hardly too much to say that at summer flow there is more wood than water in the river.

Where a channel passes through pasture lands, it should be protected by wire or other fencing against the promiscuous entry of cattle. It is easy in most cases to provide drinking places by digging pools at convenient spots along the river side, and at such depths that they shall always contain water even under summer conditions. If the channel is embanked, the embankment should be carried round the field side of the pool and ramps provided from the field to the top of the embankment and down again into the pool so that cattle may not be tempted to climb other portions of the embankment. If such pools and fences be provided there should be no need for cross-stream fences or cattle rails such as are often erected to prevent cattle straying up or down stream from one property to another. Such obstructions are a fruitful source of trouble in any channel, as they often hold up floating wrack to such an extent as to form a veritable dam across the stream.

Where a main channel intersects or flanks a low-lying area which would be liable to be inundated owing to the overflow of the river at flood periods, the lands may need to be protected by embankments, the material for which can usually be obtained from excavations in the channel. Before deciding, however, upon the construction of embankments the engineer should satisfy himself that it is impossible to secure the safety of the lands by increasing the gradient or section or both of the existing channel. For example, suppose it were found that the mean gradient of part of the channel was 2·5 feet per mile and the mean gradient of a lower part was 2 feet per mile: if it were possible by improvement of the inclination of the bed over the lower part to add another few inches of fall per mile, and if, at the same time, the sides of the channel could be battered back so as to provide more reservoir capacity for flood waters, it might not become necessary to build up artificial barriers.

Improvement Works

In a low-lying area, the channel is likely to be more sinuous than one which has a better natural fall. Where that is the case it may be good economy to cut through some of the bends so as to shorten the course and thereby increase the mean gradient. If, for example, the distance measured by the winding course of a stream between given points were found to be 1 mile and the fall over that course 6 inches, and if by straightening some of the course the length of channel could be shortened to ½ mile, the gradient would be doubled and the discharge capacity increased by about 40 per cent. It will be wise, therefore, to consider very carefully the utility and economy of making new cuts which might not need to be embanked, or whose embankments need be of no great height, rather than to form long and high embankments following the natural course of the channel, the improvement of the section of which alone might cost almost as much as the excavation of the new cuts.

In a number of instances within the author's knowledge embankments have been quite unnecessarily built when fairly obvious improvements of the channel or short new cuts were all that was required to safeguard the flanking lands. Once built, the embankments give a false sense of security, for no one then seems to pay much attention to the state of the channel. Weeds may grow unchecked in it : those weeds may screen out the silt and deposit it on the bed and slopes ; bushes or trees may grow and flourish on its cesses and islands and general deterioration may set in, with the result that both ordinary and flood flows reach higher and higher levels, each increase of level necessitating a further elevation of the height of the embankments. In many cases the beds of the streams are now actually higher than the lands which were originally sought to be protected from occasional overflow.

Where embankments are necessary, they should preferably be built at some little distance from the edge of the channel so as to leave a good forward toe of earth for the support of their weight and to increase the reservoir capacity of the flood channel. Their slopes should be, as a rule, not less than $1\frac{1}{2}$ to 1, nor their width of top less than one-eighth the base. It is usually advisable to provide the ganger in charge of the work with a number of wooden templates made to the angle required for the slopes of the embankments and to direct him that the batter is to be according to template, rather than to leave him to set out the slopes according to stated figures only.

If possible, the embankments should be cored either with puddled or dry clay as the nature of the case may demand, but in either case the work should be well rammed during construction. On completion the whole surface should be sown with grass seed.

We may now proceed to consider such parts of an arterial drainage system as may be partially closed by obstructions, such as locks, mills, sluices, dams, weirs, etc.

In such cases the natural gradient or inclined plane of the bed of the channel has been artificially converted into a series of steps, so depriving it of a very large degree of its efficiency as a drainage channel. Assuming, for example, that a river having a natural fall of 3 feet per mile is made navigable for 30 miles, the navigating vessels must climb or descend 90 feet from end to end of the navigable length. This can only be accomplished by dividing the fairway into convenient lengths, at each end of which a lock must be provided into which, say, an ascending vessel can be floated at the lower level, and then, after the lower gates have been closed and sufficient water from the higher reach let into the lock to bring the water level in its basin up to the upper reach level, the vessel can be let out through the upper gates into the higher level. If the barges or other vessels have a maximum draught, say, of 4 feet 6 inches, it may be necessary to provide at each change of level in the channel a lift of 5 feet, which would involve the conversion of the former inclined plane of 30 miles of the river into a series of eighteen steps, each with a 5 feet riser and a practically level tread.

If no other provision were made for the voidance of excess water than that of letting down a lockful whenever a vessel was going up or coming down stream, it is obvious that the upper reaches would rapidly become gorged and the banks overflowed, especially during the night or at week-ends when there was little or no traffic. It is customary, however, to provide "slackers," fitted with mechanically operable penstocks or sluice valves, either in the masonry of the lockpit or in the lock gates, whereby water can be passed into the pit for the equalization of its water level with that of the upper reach, or away down stream. In large navigation systems, where the volume of water to be voided is greater than could be sent through the slackers, drainage "eyes" fitted with sluices are provided. The sluices are drawn at night, at week-ends and at any other necessary periods to a sufficient extent to send down drainage water without impairment of the navigation heads in the several reaches of the system. In most navigation systems there are also provided weirs or tumbling bays over which any excess of water, over and above that required to maintain the navigation level, may be automatically voided into a spillway or bye-pass channel which discharges at the lower level.

In the case of an active navigation, there may not be much cause of complaint as regards the capacity or fitness of the main channel to carry off drainage water; for although it is necessary to keep up a certain head for navigation purposes, it is manifestly against the interests of the navigation authority to have their banks overflowed. In these cases, too, the channels are generally kept well dredged and free from weeds or other impediments to the free passage of water. The channels may be therefore superior as drainage conduits to those in which there is no navigation and no regular system of maintenance. Unfortunately, there are in England many navigation systems which are either utterly derelict or so little used for traffic as to be practically negligible as means of transport, and in these cases drainage has suffered very seriously.

Previously to the Railway Era, river and canal navigation naturally played a very important part in the agricultural and industrial economy of the country, and it was necessary, in adapting a river channel for traffic, either by improvement or canalization, to have due regard both to agricultural and manufacturing interests. Provision was made, therefore, not only for the transport of merchandise but for the continued drainage of lands into the new or improved channels. There are at the present time in various parts of the country, existing bodies of Drainage and Navigation Commissions whose history may date back for two or three centuries, but whose means of carrying out or maintaining works of drainage have long since disappeared in the decay of those navigation tolls which formerly constituted their principal source of revenue. The Great Ouse up to Bedford and its main tributaries the Cam, Lark, Brandon, Wissey and Ivel; the Trent from Gainsborough to Nottingham; the Witham from Boston to Lincoln and beyond; the Welland from Fosdyke to Spalding; the Nene from below Wisbech to Peterborough and beyond, are some of the many instances in which the decay of navigation has worked injuriously to drainage. In the case of the Horncastle, Caistor, Market Weighton, Pocklington, Hereford and Gloucester, River Lugg, Louth, Foss and many other small navigation and drainage systems, the navigation is to all intents and purposes non-existent, and in each case drainage conditions have become deplorable.

The author has personally inspected and reported upon five old navigation and drainage channels from which navigation had disappeared utterly and whose remaining drainage capacity was of the most woeful description. In two of these cases, modifications have been made with most satisfactory results to the affected lands, and in two other cases works of improvement have been designed which it is hoped will similarly contribute towards a restoration to prosperity of several thousand acres of excellent land which for a generation past have produced no crops.

A not unusual method of adapting a natural channel for navigation and drainage was to take advantage of the sinuosities of the river to build up artificial conduits across the loops in such manner that the water from the high level at one extremity of a bend flowed at a very slight inclination to a convenient point lower down stream where the difference of level between the artificial and natural streams would suffice for the provision of a lock. Thus, in a river having a fall of 3 feet per mile, an elevated canal might be constructed beginning at the natural level at a point A and being continued in a straight line, say, for a mile to a point B where it again met the river which, having a sinuous course measuring $1\frac{2}{3}$ miles, would be about 5 feet lower than the canal at that point. In such a case the land which previously to the construction of the elevated canal drained by gravitation across the site of the canal into the river would be cut off from the latter, so that other provisions became necessary. These provisions were made and as a rule worked admirably whilst the navigations flourished, but the decadence of canal traffic has, in a large number of instances, resulted in grave injury to drainage.

In many cases, part of the water which was diverted from its natural gradient into a canal cut was used at the lower end of the cut for power purposes by mills which were usually erected near the canal locks. In these cases the navigation and milling interests were often identical, or, where they differed, the navigation authority had a first claim on the water. In cases where navigation has failed and a certain amount of milling has survived, conditions have been less aggravated from the drainage point of view, as, although the main channels may have been greatly neglected, a certain amount of water which would otherwise have been held back to the detriment of the lands has been passed away through the mill sluices.

In improving an old navigation system for drainage purposes, it is necessary to restore as far as possible the capacity of the mother channel. An obvious way to do this is to remove the weirs or dams by means of which the water was diverted into the canal cuts so as to re-direct it into its natural course, but great care must be taken to do this in such a way that the banks of the stream above the site of the dam or weir do not slide into the channel. As has been already explained, water pressure affords a very considerable amount of lateral support to the banks of an earthen channel, and especially so where, as in the case of a canal or canalized river, the stream is so slow as to cause little erosion of the banks. If by the rash removal of an artificial obstruction the water level be suddenly lowered a few feet and a rapid stream set up in place of almost still water, the relief from lateral pressure on the banks and the undercutting action of the stream might cause serious falls for a long distance back from the old point of obstruction. This contingency must be provided against by preparing the channel for a resumption of its ancient duty. It should be carefully resectioned and regraded to the ascertained requirements both below and above the dam site before the dam is removed, and the latter operation should be commenced and continued so as at first to keep the stream as nearly as may be in the centre of the channel. With this object, the centre portion of the dam may be gradually and slowly removed to the level of the improved bed of the channel, subsequent removals proceeding outwardly from the centre to a similar level, so that the rush of the newly released stream shall not injure the sides of the course and so that the banks may have a chance of draining under more or less natural conditions of saturated earth. The operation of removal should, preferably, be carried out during or very soon after a spell of dry weather, when the water is low.

As an alternative to dismantling a weir, it may be preferable to insert a sluice which can he kept shut down when water is required to be kept up during dry spells or for milling or other purposes and drawn up during flood periods, or an automatic weir which tips up or falls down when the water has reached a pre-determined level may sometimes be fitted with advantage.

It might be convenient in some instances to improve the old canal section of a derelict navigation system so as to increase the reservoir capacity of the river as a provision for flood waters ; this may be done by restoring the sections and gradients of the artificial conduits from which the water can be discharged when convenient through the slackers or sluices at the lower locks.

Where a drainage system is sectionized or divided into compartments by mills alone, a similar effect to that produced by a navigation system is produced, viz., that the inclined plane of the river channel becomes divided into a series of steps. Water is diverted at some point from the natural channel at natural level, led into a leet or flume or dam which is built up across the land to another point on the river having a lower level, and there allowed to fall when required for power purposes through the mill sluices into the river again.

A weir is usually provided at the point of diversion from the main stream, which then becomes an overflow channel only. Any water which is not required for milling purposes can usually be passed away from the mill dam through floodgates—or, as they are sometimes termed, hatches or bolts—or, if there is no second weir, over the top of the hatches. The flood hatches and weirs in mill dams are usually so arranged that their tops coincide more or less in level with top water level at milling head ; they act automatically, therefore, as spillwaters for such volume coming down the dam as is in excess of the volume required for power purposes. The excess water goes over into a bye-pass channel or back ditch which empties itself into the natural channel of the river just below the tail race of the mill.

As with navigation, so with water-milling, the old interests have decayed, and it is no uncommon experience to find that of a number of mills on a single river, each of which may in its time have done a lucrative trade in flour-milling from locally grown crops, some are in ruins, others used merely as dwelling-houses, and the small remainder eking out a bare subsistence by gristing or wood-sawing.

At no time, probably, were drainage provisions by mill streams as satisfactory as those by navigation channels, because there was little or no correlation of interests. Whereas a navigation authority were obliged to construct their works in accordance with the requirements of their special

Act of Parliament, any landowner who happened to possess a portion of a river channel was at liberty to adapt it for milling and to make only such provisions for the voidance of excess water as seemed to him sufficient to prevent flooding of the mill floor.

The probability is that the various mills on any river were built at different times by different owners, and that very few calculations entered into the arrangements for the automatic and equivalent discharge of flood flows of the river as a whole. An instance of the chaotic conditions which may sometimes obtain in a " milled " river is to be found on the Waveney between Hoxne and Ellingham, where there are eleven mills at which the waterway openings over the crests of the weirs are as follows: Hoxne, 35 feet 6 inches; Syleham, 16 feet 3 inches; Needham, 18 feet 6 inches; Weybread, 19 feet 6 inches; Mendham, 18 feet 3 inches; Wortwell, 20 feet 8 inches (two); Homersfield, 18 feet 8 inches; Earsham, 7 feet; Bungay, 13 feet 6 inches and 17 feet; Wainford, 16 feet; and Ellingham, 18 feet 9 inches. Hoxne Mill is at the upper end of the series, and it was apparently considered by those who provided the weirway there that a crest length of 35 feet 6 inches was necessary for the discharge of any surplus water above milling head. Those who settled the dimensions at Syleham next below it appear to have thought that about half that length would suffice; different views expressed themselves lower down stream, until at

Earsham it was decided that about one-fifth the Hoxne length would suffice, and yet Bungay next below Hoxne needed 30 feet 6 inches to pass the water on to Wainford through 16 feet to Ellingham! Height of crest is not material, as this is of course relative to milling head in each case. Need it be stated that some of the mills are occasionally short of water, whilst at the same time others are flooded.

The mill sluices and floodgates would of course pass large volumes of water when open, but weirs cannot come into full operation at such times. It is for the automatic discharge of excess water during non-working hours and at flood times that weirs are chiefly required.

The absence of co-ordination of control of mill streams often expresses itself in a total neglect of the channels. After having inspected many scores of mill streams with a view to their improvement as drainage channels, the author is unable to recall an instance where weed-cutting and hand dredging of the mill dam were regularly carried out. The answer to any remonstrance is that, if those above or below do not keep their portions of the channel clean, it would be useless for the miller or owner immediately concerned to do anything.

Millers are often and somewhat undeservedly blamed for holding back water which, owing to the obstructed state of the channel, does not, in fact, reach their mills. When streams above the mills overtop their banks and flood the lands, the fault is commonly attributed to lack of proper regulation of the mill sluices ; whereas the fact may be that, except at periods of exceptional flood, the mills are short of water. The obstructive effect of a heavily weeded channel might well surprise those who have not carried out tests. As an instance, the whole of the very adequate sluices at Dedham Mill on the Essex Stour were, at the author's request, kept fully drawn from midnight until 9.30 a.m., during which period the lower portion of the mill dam had been emptied of 5 feet of water, whilst the water level at Stratford St. Mary Mill, about 1 mile upstream, had been reduced by 3 inches only.

As a consequence of neglect of mill-stream channels, millers are often tempted to hold up water to a higher level than that represented by the proper milling head ; this is done by placing wooden " floats " or " flashers " on the crests of the weirs and " paddles " on the flood hatches. These devices serve to arrest for power purposes water which should be automatically voided, but it is common to find that the flashers and paddles are left in position during non-working hours, with the results that banks are overflowed or breached and that mills at lower levels are deprived of their quota of water.

Given clean and properly sectioned channels, millers are far from being interested in holding water above milling head, except perhaps in very dry weather, when the total volume descending the channel is small. In other conditions high levels are very troublesome to millers, for if flood water is passed away through the flood hatches as rapidly as it comes down, it may "back up" in the tail race, so creating an adverse head against the wheel and stopping the mill, to say nothing of the flooding of the mill premises.

Improvements of mill streams for drainage purposes should generally follow the lines recommended for old navigation channels, except that where milling interests had to be maintained it would be impossible to remove weirs or dams at the points of diversion from the mother stream. All weirs, dams, sluices or hatches, however, should be overhauled with a view to such necessary modifications as may insure full provision for the automatic discharge of all water which is not passed through mill-wheel sluices during working hours.

Weirs fitted with sluices which can be drawn at flood times, or falling weirs, the crests of which can be temporarily lowered so as to afford a larger than normal discharge, may sometimes be provided with advantage. Weirs that may be required to be maintained at a fixed crest level should, as a rule, be built obliquely across the stream with a length equal to about three to three and a half times the mean width of the channel immediately above them and with a crest of parabolic section. This form has been proved by the experience of many years in the Severn to give a better discharge per foot of length than that for flat-crested weirs.

CHAPTER IX

SLUICES

WHERE a main channel which is liable to periodical or sudden alternations of water level is entered by tributary channels of flat gradient, it is necessary to make provision against the flooding of the latter by the waters of the former. Suppose, for example, that a tributary channel brings water for a considerable distance across land whose lowest or general level is below that of high water of tides or floods in the main channel, and that no provision were made for the exclusion from the channel of the higher level water, the lands in the tributary valley must be liable to tidal flow and ebb from the main channel, or, if the main channel be non-tidal, to occasional flooding due to any circumstance which produces gorging in the main channel.

The necessity here is to provide a barrier against the influx of main channel water whilst leaving adequate means of egress for tributary water, and to provide in the tributary channel sufficient reservoir capacity to contain the low level water without overflow of the banks until the water level in the main channel has fallen sufficiently to allow the tributary to discharge.

The word " sluice " is generally used to denote any one of a whole set of appliances provided for the periodical discharge of water in such circumstances. It may be as well, therefore, briefly to particularize them. A " sluice," properly so called, is a sliding gate fitted into a frame within which the gate can be raised or lowered for the voidance or retention of water.

The word " staunch," which is often rather loosely used to denote a sluice of the kind just described, or indeed any other kind of sluice, is more properly descriptive of an apparatus which is sometimes used instead of a lock to hold up a head of water for navigation purposes. It usually comprises a wooden sluice-gate hung from a top frame by chains passing over pulleys, and is operated by a winch or two winches worked by hand. When a vessel is to be passed under the staunch, the gate is gradually lifted and the water from the upper reach is allowed to pass away under it until a common level is reached. A staunch can only be used in comparatively small channels and for vessels without masts or other top hamper.

A " clough," or " tidal flap," or " tankard lid," is a door suspended by hinges from the top of an outwardly tilted frame against which the door rests normally or under the pressure of an outside head of water. A superior head of water on the inside, however, pushes the door open and allows discharge to take place. A clough may be compared to an ordinary room door which instead of being hinged on one side is hinged to the top of the door frame, the bottom edge of the door, however, closing against a cill or fourth member of the door frame so that water from the outside cannot pass under it as it might in the case of a room door which usually has no bottom framing. Cloughs are not much used for main outfalls, but are very largely used in connection with low level drainage. The best form of clough is that which is provided with a counterweight so adjusted that barely any part of the weight of the flap can operate against the water in the drain.

Tidal gates, or pointing doors comprise a pair of doors hung to side frames in much the same manner as ordinary swing doors, but closing together at an obtuse angle against V-shaped frames at top and bottom, the bottom frame being the cill and the top frame the hood. These doors point outward towards the side from which high-level water might enter, so that when the hydraulic head on that side is superior to the head on the inner side of the doors the latter are pushed to by the pressure and remain closed, edge to edge, and sealed at bottom, top and sides against the framing until the outside head has fallen sufficiently to allow the inside head to push them open again. In order that the outside head may operate with certainty and rapidity, the doors are set so that they cannot open to a full waterway, buffer beams or some other convenient provision being made to give them a slight inclination towards each other when at their full outward swing. Without some such provision the pressure of water on the outer side might operate against the inner faces of the doors, so forcing them open instead of closing them.

It will be seen that whereas sluices and staunches as above defined depend upon manual manipulation for their action, cloughs and pointing doors act automatically, opening for the discharge of water from behind them when the back head of water is superior to the front head and closing when the front head is superior to the back head.

In choosing the site for the erection of a "sluice," great care must be taken to estimate the probabilities of siltation on the "apron," or, as one may illustrate it, the doorstep in front of the cill of automatic cloughs or pointing doors. Great trouble has been experienced at the sluice outfalls along the River Trent, for instance, owing to the heavy and rapid accumulations of "warp" within the short outfall channels between the doors and the main channel. Although these channels may be only a few yards in length, they become so foul with silt after only a few tides that masses of almost impalpable mud are piled up against the lower parts of the doors, so preventing them from opening in response to the pressure of water in the drainage channels behind them. It is probable that had this contingency been more fully appreciated at the outset the sluices would have been built almost flush with the side of the main channel. Suggestions have been made that even now these sluices should be brought forward the necessary distance to ensure their faces being swept by the tidal waters of the Trent, or, alternatively, that short outfall tunnels from the sluices to the river should be constructed with as steep an outward slope as possible in order that whilst there would be less opportunity for the lodgment of silt, the shape of the tunnel would provide a more concentrated and powerful scouring stream when the sluices were discharging. So far, however, nothing has been done in either direction

The outfall channel at the Middle Level Sluice which discharges into the Great Ouse at Wiggenhall also accumulates vast quantities of silt which has periodically to be dredged out at considerable expense. It is generally advisable where possible to place the outfall sluice at a concave bend of the river where the scour is best and the depth greatest.

It is probable that in the case of main channels which do not carry large amounts of solids in suspension, some advantage is gained by the placement of sluices at a little distance back from the river side, for the sluice doors are not then so subject to the influence of swirls and eddies and the collection of floating wrack as they might be near to the main stream. The movement of the doors should, of course, be as regular and easy as conditions may allow, for they would become liable to injury if subject to any violent influence causing them to be thrown suddenly together.

It may be mentioned in this connection that the ordinary method of hanging pointing doors on their framing leaves something to be desired. The weight of the doors, sometimes several tons, has a tendency to throw an oblique strain on the hinge pins and eyes which causes the doors to sink slightly out of their original alignment, so that instead of moving towards each other with ease and simultaneity, as soon as the outside head rises above the inside head, one or other of them may stick, and then, later, when the pressure becomes too great for further frictional resistance, the door is so suddenly and violently thrown against the framing as to jeopardize the security of the whole structure. At South Ferriby, the outfall of the River Ancholme into the Humber, it is necessary, owing to such circumstances, for the sluice keeper to be in attendance whenever the rising tide reaches cill level in order that he may ease the doors towards each other. On an occasion when the man was unable to be on duty the doors stuck against the rising tide so long that when they did move they came together with "a report like a cannon that was heard miles away." To counteract such defects the author has designed a set of balanced doors moving on ball-thrust footstep bearings, but the efficiency of the design has not yet been tested under actual service conditions.

Where both navigation and drainage have to be dealt with at the main channel end of a large tributary river or canal, it is usual to provide drainage eyes distinct from the navigation eyes or locks. These may consist of the necessary number of pairs of pointing doors alone or having behind them framed sluice gates which can be opened or closed at will.

In the case of a canal drainage system, it is not unusual to find that sluice gates have been provided inside the site of the outfall doors, as it is sometimes necessary to conserve for navigation purposes some of the water which would escape automatically through the doors if there were no means of arresting it. In other than canal systems, sluices forming a second line of defence are occasionally fitted inside the doors, and these are sometimes used to pen up a sufficient head of water in the tributary or main drain to flush the outfall channel of accumulations of silt when the sluices are drawn. It must be said that, although such extra provisions are necessarily costly in first outlay, they prove to be of inestimable value in the event of any sudden injury to the outfall doors necessitating a rapid closure of the tributary against the incursion of tidal or high level river water. There is no doubt either of their value for local flushing purposes, for whereas the automatic doors should open with a head of an inch or less and as the water passing through at that head has only a very low velocity, the penning up of the stream behind the sluice gates to a head of 2 or 3 feet will provide a stream of cascading effect in a short outfall channel.

In the case of an outfall sluice into a tideway, it is necessary to calculate the effective areas of the openings by reference to the volume to be passed away during the limited periods during which the doors can remain open, and, either in this case or in the case of a non-tidal channel subject to sudden spate conditions, to arrange that the tributary channel shall have sufficient capacity to retain the water until outside circumstances allow it to get away. If the tributary channel traverses low-lying land, it may not be possible to give it anything but a low gradient, nor may it be possible to section it to any great depth, as it is obvious that, however low its gradient, the inclination must be sufficient to ensure that the water will flow from the lowest portion of the level, and that to form the bed at a low initial level at that lowest portion and to incline the bed downwards towards the outfall sluice might bring the bed at that point too far below the cill. Cill-levels should preferably be kept down to or only very slightly above the lowest low-water level in the main channel. In some cases it may be desirable even to place them only just above the bed of the channel, but there is often only a very small choice between depth plus gradient and width for the tributary channel, and in such cases the position of the cill is dictated rather than chosen.

The outfall channels of sluices should, as a rule, point in the direction of the flow of the stream if the discharge be into a river, or in the direction of the ebb if the discharge be into a tidal channel. The smaller the angle formed between the outfall channel and the main channel, the less will be the impediment offered by the main channel water to the outflow, and the smaller will be the chance of silt or wrack lodging on the apron.

The volume of water that will be discharged by a sluice in a given period is the product of the area of the waterway into the velocity of the stream minus an allowance for friction due to the particular form of sluice used.

State of "channel" of River Kyle, above Alne, before cleansing operations were commenced *(see p. 26)*

Commencing cleansing operations, River Kyle, near Alne

Breach in tidal embankment of Littlehampton Harbour caused by exceptionally high tide,
16th January, 1918

(Owing to a sudden reduction of atmospheric pressure the last 5 feet of the tidal elevation took place in 30 minutes.) *(see p. 58)*

Breach in tidal embankment of River Arun caused by exceptionally high tide, 16th January, 1918

(Owing to a sudden reduction of atmospheric pressure the last 5 feet of the tidal elevation took place in 30 minutes.)

Digging out old-established weed roots, River Kyle *(see p. 84)*

Resectioning and regrading the channel after removal of obstructions, River Kyle

Picturesque intruders, River Foss, near Yearsley *(see p. 88)*

A derelict navigation channel, River Foss, near Strensall *(see p. 94)*

River Ivel at Beeston, before improvement works were commenced, showing contraction of the channel due to siltation *(see p. 120)*

Prisoners of war removing sludge from bed of River Ivel near Girtford Bridge, Sandy

Channel of River Ivel below Tempsford Mill, after improvement *(see p. 122)*

Channel of River Ivel above Tempsford Mill,
after improvement, showing concrete apron
put in to protect a specially weak section of the bank

Channel of River Ivel near Blunham Rectory,
after improvement *(see p. 124)*

CHAPTER X

STRUCTURAL AND OTHER IMPEDIMENTS TO FLOW

THE necessity of ample provisions of sectional area and gradient of main channels and their main feeders has been already emphasized, but one of the most fruitful sources of trouble to the drainage engineer, viz., the occurrence of road and railway bridges or fords crossing an arterial or other channel, has so far been only very briefly touched upon.

It is unfortunately the fact that highway authorities, railway companies and private owners who may have had a right to build bridges or culverts across waterways have not in all cases arranged their structures with due regard to the drainage requirements of the channels. In the same way, those responsible for the provision and maintenance of a hard surface across a ford have not, as a rule, paid very much attention to the circumstance that by raising the bed of the stream in line with the roadway they may be forming a seriously injurious dam.

As regards bridges, the author has often found that masonry piers have been built either in the channel itself or with their inner faces rising from the immediate sides of the bed of the channel, thus leaving no room for lateral expansion of the water at flood times, or that very low semicircular or pointed arches have been constructed with their springing from the ends of a chord which may possibly satisfy the æsthetic eye of the bridge architect, but is far too short to satisfy the practical requirements of the drainage engineer.

Whilst some concession to taste may perhaps be made in the case of the architect, it is difficult to find excuses for railway engineers who, however concentrated may be their interests on other subjects than drainage, might be reasonably expected to give some little consideration to the fact that moving bodies other than trains require an unobstructed roadway. It must be said, however, that railway engineers are among the worst offenders when provision for running water is in question.

The plain fact is that those who design or construct railway bridges or culverts are allowed by the Standing Orders of Parliament to do pretty much as they like in such matters. The word "culvert" may certainly appear at its proper place on the parliamentary plans, but it is not held necessary to give either its shape or dimensions or invert level, and not a word of any of these has, so far as the author has had experience, ever appeared in a railway bill. It is true that a bridge may have its span dimensions marked on the plan, but Private Bill Examiners and Private Bill Committees alike appear to be indifferent to the fact that, once passed, the Act authorizing construction may give the Company a statutory right virtually to dam the river by building the invert of the bridge or culvert at any level convenient to themselves without any regard to the effect upon the lands along the valley above the structure. It should certainly be required that every proposed new bridge or culvert should be of ample dimensions and of sufficiently low invert level to pass the maximum volume of water due to the run-off of the area above the structure. Even if it were not required to give dimensions and levels on the plans and sections, verbal provisions to that effect should be inserted in the bills.

Wherever bridge or culvert waterways are found to be insufficient and it is impracticable to rebuild the structure, it may be found possible by arrangement with the authorities or persons concerned to add pipeways of sufficient area to pass the required additional volume.

It may sometimes be possible to adopt the alternative of one or more bye-pass channels or loops to pass through short tunnels under the road or railway as the case may be; but in any case it would be manifestly fatal to drainage to allow such obstructions as insufficient bridge arches or culverts to go by default, and although much ingenuity, tact and negotiation may be necessary in such cases, the engineer should exhaust all possibilities before abandoning his case for a full waterway.

A device which may occasionally be adopted, but which has not much to recommend it, is that of an inverted syphon or trunk in the form of a laterally elongated letter U. Water which enters at the upper end will rise to the same level in the lower end, and as this may be arranged at a few inches lower level the discharge will be ensured so long as the horizontal portion of the syphon is free to act as a conduit. Inverted syphons are, however, extremely liable to get choked up with silt and debris, and for that reason should be resorted to only after other means have been found impossible.

There is usually less difficulty with fords whose top surfaces are too high in relation to the rest of the bed of the channel, for there are few cases in which it would not be possible to reconstruct the ford to a satisfactory level for traffic by inserting beneath it a number of ferro-concrete or iron pipes and topping them with concrete to a sufficient thickness to ensure their stability against fracture by ordinary road vehicles. If, however, the ford is likely to be at any time used for steam or other heavy vehicles such as traction engines or lorries, it might be necessary to strengthen the concrete topping with steel joist or rail reinforcement. If concrete pipes be used, it may be desirable to construct them as very finely tapering hollow cones and to lay them with the narrower ends up stream. Pipes so constructed and laid are less likely than cylindrical pipes to get blocked up by floating wrack, or if they do become blocked during dry seasons they will be more readily scoured out by flood flows.

There remains to be mentioned one other cause of possible impediment, and that an insidious one, because it is not uncommonly disguised. Wherever there is sand in the soil of the drainage area, whether in natural beds or mixed with loam or gravel, quantities of it will get washed out into the various drainage channels, where, owing to its high specific gravity, it will sink to the bottom wherever the slowness of the carrying stream will allow. Once deposited, it appears as a clean, flat waterfloor over which the stream passes with delightful smoothness ; or it may arrange itself conformably within the hollows between shoals, generally reducing the apparent height of the latter until what was an undulating and uneven bed has become one of planic regularity.

In all cases of slowly moving streams through sandy soils, sand traps should be provided. These may be placed near the outfall end of the particular channel affected so as to confine the trouble to that channel. A sand trap may consist of a masonry, concrete or timber pit having a sloping base and three sides, two of which taper from nothing to the full depth of the back end of the trap, somewhat after the shape of an ordinary coal scoop. This is sunk into the bed of the channel at some suitable point below the lowest point of ingress of the sand, the lip of the trap pointing up-stream. The width of the trap should be that of the channel, and its depth at the lower end sufficient to collect whatever quantities of sand may be estimated to be caught within whatever periods may be settled as convenient between one emptying and another.

It may not be inappropriate to suggest that well-washed sharp river sand has a commercial value, and that, given a convenient market, sand traps should yield a very respectable return upon their cost, besides saving cost in other directions.

CHAPTER XI

MAINTENANCE OF ARTERIAL CHANNELS

BEFORE leaving the subject of Arterial Drainage, it may be as well to offer a few remarks upon the necessity and manner of maintenance of new or improved channels.

Assuming that sectional areas and gradients are approximately as they should be; that the sides of the channel are sufficiently battered to be proof against slipping and to afford reservoir capacity for flood waters; that embankments have been properly formed at the proper distance from the edge of the channel; that the artery and its earthen walls have been fenced against cattle for which proper drinking pools have been provided; that there are no cattle fences or other obstructions across the stream; that bridge openings, culverts and fords which might offer resistance have been improved; that old locks, mills, dams, sluices or other obstructions have been modified; that any necessary sand traps have been provided, and generally that the system as a whole has been restored to order, some regular provision should be made for its due and proper maintenance.

Maintenance of Arterial Channels

This may seem too obvious a thing to say or write, but the laxity or ignorance sometimes shown even by properly constituted drainage authorities towards ordinary maintenance is astounding.

In no case should trees or bushes be allowed to occupy any part of the channel, its forelands, washes, or embankments. Apart from the physical obstruction which ingrowing or overhanging trees may offer to flood flows, their root leverage during windy weather has a very disintegrating effect on the banks. Given an uprooting gale, there will nearly always be more river than other trees blown down, and these, owing to their usual riverward tilt, will probably fall into or across the channel. Bushes are not liable to injure banks or to be thrown into the channel, but they often form even greater impediments to the stream than trees.

Weeds should be regularly cut at stated periods. The neglect of systematic weed-cutting, or "roding," spells disaster to any channel. Once the growth becomes established, the weeds act as sieves or screens or filters sifting out the suspended solids and throwing them down in the form of soft sludge to the bed of the channel, there to receive and propagate the spores of the mother weeds and give rise to further and heavier growths. Weeds must either not be allowed to establish themselves or must be ruthlessly grubbed out if a good stream is to be maintained. It may perhaps suffice to cut the weeds twice annually, say in May and October, but it would certainly be better to arrange not only for three regular rodings but to rake out any sporadic growths as they appear. If the weeds are well grown, they may be usually cut off close to the bed of the channel by means of scythe blades fixed to long handles worked from a boat or punt. The work should be begun at the lower end of the channel and continued in an up-stream direction, temporary barriers of stakes with rope connections arranged just below the water-line being placed across the stream to catch the detached masses as they float down. Weeds should not be left on or near the banks, but should be gathered together, air-dried and then burnt. After each cutting, the bed of the channel should be raked with long-handled steel rakes having sharp prongs and afterwards cleaned up with flat-bladed river scoops for the removal of mud.

The dredgings or scoopings should not be left upon the sides of the channel, where they would be likely to be washed in again during floods, but spread on the land where they might have some manurial value, or added to the banks or tops and slopes of the embankments.

It is possible, in the case of small streams, to carry out most of the work of clearance from the sides by means of tools with long handles or fixed to chains or ropes worked by men standing on opposite sides of the channel and dragging the tools across it. In large streams, boats or punts may be necessary, and where that is the case it may be desirable to provide power for occasional dredging or eroding. In dredging from a boat there may be some inconvenience in disposing of the solids brought up into the vessel, but this inconvenience must not be allowed to outweigh the necessity when once that has been proved. Equally good results can sometimes be achieved with an eroder which, working up-stream, will scarify the bottom of the channel and stir up into suspension masses of solids which, given a good stream, will be carried away to the outfall.

It may be objected that if eroding is begun at the lower end of the channel, the up-stream solids will re-collect on the portion already cleaned. This is the less likely, however, as the effect of bottom eroding is to deepen the channel, and it has been previously pointed out that increased depth gives increased velocity in proportion to the square root of the depth ; the eroded portion will therefore give a higher velocity than the uneroded portion, and any solids in suspension which can successfully negotiate the shallower parts of the channel will be pretty sure to pass the deeper.

Any slippings of or accidental injury to banks should be at once repaired and the side slopes maintained intact. Embankments should be frequently examined for settlement or injury and restored to standard height and slope where these are found to be defective. The overtopping of an embankment at a single part by flood water may easily result in wholesale inundation of the lands behind, as, owing to the slope of the back of the embankment, the water will scour out for itself a deep channel, so reducing the strength of the embankment at that point as to jeopardize the security of the whole mass. Once through a gap so caused, the water will continue to widen the breach until flood power is exhausted. Moles, rats and rabbits must be remorselessly kept down. The danger from the burrowings of vermin is so well recognized in the Fen country that some of the molecatchers who had been regularly and continuously employed in destroying these pests were, for a long period after the Military Service Act came into operation, exempted from service as indispensable. The vermin multiply at an incredible rate if left undisturbed, and the injury they cause is incalculable. What has been said of the danger of depressed embankments is only a little of the truth when compared with the danger of honeycombed embankments. A depression can be seen from afar, but a burrowed embankment which appears fair to the eye may be little fitter to resist lateral thrust than a bandbox.

In any system which depends largely for its security upon embankments, men should be regularly employed to examine the banks and lay snares at all the burrows, or, if necessary, to dig out the vermin wherever they may be. At one period the mole catchers of the Fens were paid so much per hundred head of vermin brought in; but this practice has long been abandoned, since it was discovered that some of the men bred the animals wholesale and could produce for the pay tally as many heads or tails as their pocket needs demanded. Serious breaches which, if not directly traceable to the ravages of vermin, might have been contributed to by them, occurred in 1830, 1831, 1837, 1872, 1877, 1880, 1882, 1897 and 1910 in the embankments of the River Glen, an upland water tributary of the Welland, which is embanked for many miles across Deeping Fen to an average height above the fen of about 10 feet. Very serious breaches have also occurred from time to time in the fen defences of the South Level in Norfolk. The most disastrous in recent years was that which happened in the Feltwell district in 1915, when the Northern embankment of the Little Ouse or Brandon River burst during a period of high river flood when at the same time an exceptionally high tide below Denver sluice sealed the sluice against outward relief. On that occasion, practically the whole mass of the barrier was carried away for a length of about 150 yards, the river pouring through the gap until about 19,000 acres of land were flooded to an average depth of 4 feet. The damage caused by that disaster was variously estimated at from £150,000 to £200,000.

Lastly, strict attention should be paid to any mechanical appliances upon which any part of the system may depend for the utterance of water. Flood gates or sluices at mills ; slackers at navigation locks or other devices for the artificial impoundment of water should be kept drawn during non-working hours or so regulated that in no case should the milling or navigation or other legitimate head be exceeded. Approaches to weirs, tumbling bays or spill waters should be frequently examined for weeds or accumulations of floating wrack or side growths and cleared as often as may be necessary; sand traps should be regularly emptied. In short, the system should be kept *open* from end to end.

The Japanese have a proverb " Paint costs nothing "; the English equivalent is " A stitch in time saves nine." Both proverbs express the wisdom of forethought and timely action to prevent deterioration of the fabric. *Verb. sap.*

CHAPTER XII

LOW-LEVEL DRAINAGE

THERE are, in England, many thousands of acres of land whose general level is below that of high water at sea. This is notably the case in the great Fen districts of Norfolk, Cambridge, Huntingdon and the Isle of Ely known as the Bedford Level, the drainage of which was first seriously undertaken in the seventeenth century under the auspices of Francis, Earl of Bedford.

Most of these lands are of peat or peaty loam, indicating that they have rotted down from scrub under the action of water which may have originally formed the swamps in which the vegetable matter which now constitutes so rich a proportion of their soil grew and flourished. The city of Ely, rising out of the surrounding fenland and now approached by good roads and a good railway, was at one period veritably an isle. References in Kingsley's *Hereward the Wake* to the swamps of the Isle of Ely may serve to remind us of the conditions which prevailed in Saxon times, and to offer a comparison with existing conditions after the execution of the great works of drainage which have done such great things for the Fens.

The "Adventurers" who, led by the enterprising Earl of Bedford, first attacked the mighty task of the drainage of the Fens, set an example of faith in works which should certainly encourage any of their successors who may be faced with lesser problems.

When the great work was begun, the lands were considerably higher than at present. The elimination of water, originally by means of great cuts draining by gravitation and later by pumping, has had the effect of causing subsidence to an astonishing degree. Up to the middle of last century, Whittlesea Mere near Ramsey, which offers a more recent example of subsidence, was, as its name indicates, a shallow lake or swamp. Since it was drained it has subsided about 10 feet.

In dealing with the subject of low-level or internal drainage, therefore, one of the most important considerations is the effect which the execution of any proposed works will have upon the levels of the lands to be drained.

In discussing the needs of the main arteries reference has been made only to such channels as form conduits for upland water. We have now to consider the best means of draining surplus water from areas which owing to their low general elevation would be otherwise permanent or temporary lakes or swamps or which, in the best of ordinary circumstances, would be chronically waterlogged.

The word "Waterlogging" may need some broad definition, and, although even skilled agriculturists might be found to differ as to a single interpretation, it may be fairly safe to say that any land, light or heavy, in which the saturation level, or " soc," is within 18 inches of the surface is waterlogged.

If, as is probable, it is desired subsequently to underdrain the low-level lands by means of tile, stone or brushwood drains, so that they shall discharge their water more rapidly and effectually than by soil seepage, it will be necessary to form any new drainage cuts or channels with as deep a bed as is consistent with a good gradient ; it will be necessary at the outset, therefore, to take careful levels over the whole of the area to be drained in order that full data may be available before any new system is laid out on plan.

In the probable event of a level of any appreciable catchment area being fringed by rising ground, it may be very desirable to take the first line of levels along the extreme margin of the level at the bottom of the lowest slopes of the hills in order to find out whether it may be possible to form along that line a catchwater drain or—as it is called in Holland—a " ringvat," the purpose of which is to arrest the water flowing off the higher ground and to direct it by a circuitous course to some convenient outfall point in the nearest arterial channel rather than allow it to add to the volume due to the level itself. It is worth the exercise of some ingenuity to keep upland and low-level water quite apart, as it will be found that the low-level drains of an ordinary marsh or fen level are generally taxed to their utmost capacity during exceptionally wet periods, and that the addition of water from the rapidly discharging hill areas may make all the difference between bank-full drains and inundation of the level.

One of the most notable instances in England of a catchwater drain is that of the Carr Dyke, the site of which traverses the line of the foot-hills between Lincoln and Peterborough. It was constructed by the Romans principally as a canal, but also with the object of collecting upland water from the western watershed of the Witham and conveying it into the Nene. It is at the present time almost obliterated and perfectly useless for either of its original purposes. The water which was formerly trapped by and discharged down its channel now flows by means of delphs across the low-lying fen lands on its eastern side into the Witham. At periods of exceptional rainfall, the delphs, which have very low gradients, become rapidly overcharged and floods inevitably ensue. Suggestions have been repeatedly made that the Carr Dyke should be re-opened for the relief of the lands along the western bank of the Witham, but other interests have, so far, prevented any action being taken.

Cors-y-bol Marsh, Anglesey, containing an area of about 1,300 acres, was originally protected against the influx of upland water by catchwater drains which ran on either side of the marsh in a direction more or less parallel with the channel of the River Alaw, into which the lower ends of the catchwaters discharged at points below the Marsh. Owing to the breaking up of the estate into a number of ownerships, the catchwaters (as well as the low-level drains) have been neglected for many years and are now no longer effectual as highland water traps. As a consequence, the Marsh, which at one time constituted a very fine feeding ground for Welsh cattle, is little better than a bog. Measures have been recently taken to remedy the conditions.

Levelling for a catchwater drain may conveniently start from the proposed point of its discharge and be continued by staff position trials along the proposed course so that the track may rise at a more or less even gradient to the terminal point. Unless the rising ground is more than commonly "humpy," it will usually be found possible to run a fairly evenly curved line, but it may be better to take a somewhat sinuous course rather than take the line through mounds of any appreciable height. There should be no reason why, in ordinary circumstances, the line of a catchwater drain should not have a perfectly even inclination, and it would be advisable where possible that this should be not less than 3 feet to a mile. It is quite unlikely that the marsh or fen drains will have anything like that gradient, and it will be desirable to pass away down the catchwater and into the arterial channel the more rapidly moving hill water, ahead of the more slowly discharging low-level water.

If sufficient levelling has been done over the low-lying area, it should be possible to prepare a map of the contours and from these to determine the best courses for the low-level cuts. When these have been tentatively laid down on the map, they should be specially levelled on the ground for the ascertainment of the lowest point in each line. The steepest possible gradient of each drain will be fixed by the difference in level between its depth below the lowest part of the surface in its line of direction upward and its depth at the point of discharge. In some instances it may be found impossible to obtain more than a fractional fall for the bed of the drain, in which case velocity must be created by providing a fall in the surface levels.

The lines of the main drains having been determined, the lines of the feeding drains may be ascertained partly by levelling and partly by considerations of convenience, such as the physical division of the lands into parcels of convenient size and shape. If drainage considerations only were present, it might be best to lead the feeders into the mains at a coarse angle whose apex pointed in the direction of the outfall, as the total length of all the drains arranged in that way would be less and their average gradient greater than if arranged in parallelograms; but sharp corners in fields are generally inconvenient, and it may be better on the whole to arrange for the feeders to fall into the mains more or less at right angles.

No two feeders from opposite sides should be taken into a main at the same point. If by their general direction they would otherwise do so, one of them—e.g., that with the better fall—should be slightly curved near its end, so as to fall into the main at a little distance below the other.

Both mains and feeders should be laid down with the view of getting the water away with the utmost rapidity, and it is better sometimes to arrange for several mains, each having its own outfall and its own system of feeders, than to throw the whole duty of conveyance upon one very large main whose feeders may need to be of great length and slowness of delivery.

The choice of points of outfall must necessarily be fixed by reference to conditions of normal water levels in the artery which is to receive the water, and it might not be possible to obtain a good discharge into the artery in a direct line with the length of the main. If, for example, the best line for the main due to the ascertained levels of the land were at right angles with the artery, but that it were found that below that point the bed of the artery had a better gradient than just at the point, advantage should be taken of that circumstance to get in at the lower level.

The direction gradient and minimum depth of a main drain having been determined, the line should be "boned out" with sight rails placed at intervals of a few chains and levelled for depth from the surface at each point so marked. At a suitable stage of the subsequent proceedings pits can be dug to finished bottom level at these points and the remainder of the bed cut to join them.

Approach to Outfall

Although catchwater drains need not and often cannot be straight, the mains and feeders of a level area should depart as little from straight lines as circumstances will allow. The velocity of the water traversing them will necessarily be low in any case, and for this reason, if for no other, unnecessary bends should be avoided. It may be found necessary, however, in order to obtain access to a good outfall point, to take a main along a course more or less parallel with the artery until some point in the latter is reached at which its normal or average water-level will permit of a good discharge. If for the reason that the general direction of the artery is away from the main drain and that the course of the latter, following that of the former, would be very long, it may be advisable to take the main across the line of the artery, so as to reach the direct outfall point by a shorter line having a better gradient. For example, if the shape of the artery in the neighbourhood of the level were that of the letter C, and the main approached it from the middle of the back of the letter without being able to get a good outfall there, it might be advisable to take the line across the letter to the lowest point in its curve rather than to follow round the curve. This would of course involve the provision of a closed conduit under the bed of the artery, which, however objectionable or difficult as compared with an open cut, might offer the best means of obtaining the necessary discharge.

The engineer's determination of the number,

direction, gradients, and sectional areas of the mains and feeders must be arrived at by reference to their capacity to discharge practically the whole of the winter rainfall of the level.

In discussing the discharge capacity necessary for an arterial system, 1 per cent. of the average annual rainfall was mentioned as a sufficient maximum for the whole of the lands, comprising uplands, midlands and lowlands; but it is obvious that, in any considerable catchment area, such as that of our supposed half-million acres, some will contribute more and others less in a given time than that due to their area measured in acres. Their greater or less permeability or their greater or smaller departure from the horizontal will necessarily affect the proportion which their average run-off bears to the total. Whilst retaining, therefore, our figure for the total run-off, we may need to make provision in the marsh or fen areas for the circumstance that in winter they evaporate scarcely any of their rainfall and that owing to their depressed level practically none of it can soak away.

Supposing catchwater drains to have been designed to take away any upland water which might otherwise have to be dealt with in addition to that due to the level, the area of the level is all that need be considered; if, however, upland water is to be added, provision must be made for it not only in the mains but in the feeders, because the water in the latter which would normally be moving downward towards the mains would be "backed up" whenever, owing to spate conditions in the uplands, high-level water was being sent down the main channels.

A heavy rainfall does not necessarily produce flood conditions in a flat area. If the rain occurs after a spell of dry weather a large proportion of it sinks into the ground, and some time may elapse during the period of exceptional wetness before the land becomes saturated. When, however, the rain is continuous over a long period or occurs after the soil is fully charged, floods must result.

It is in order to prevent or relieve flood conditions that the various factors should be principally determined, but some maximum level of saturation for ordinary conditions of climate and seasons should also be fixed before the final provisions are made.

It may be convenient in light absorbent soils, where the outward percolation also is good, to arrange for more or larger drains than in heavy soils where very little more than surface discharge has to be dealt with in a given time; but it should generally be arranged that the normal level of the water remaining in the cuts during dry weather represents a saturation level in the lands of not more than 18 inches. This is the irreducible minimum if the soil is to be regarded as other than "wet," and anything up to 3 feet 6 inches is better. If it is fairly certain that the land will be kept under grass, 24 inches might be a safe level; if, however, it is to be cultivated,

3 feet 6 inches is not too low for the saturation level.

Owing to capillary attraction and frictional resistance of the soil, the saturation level will be slightly higher than the water level in the drains. If, therefore, it be decided to leave the summer saturation level at, say, 30 inches below the surface of the soil, the bottom levels and areas of the drainage cuts must be arranged so as to leave the normal water level in the cuts at about 33 inches below the surface. If the land, light or heavy, is likely to be underdrained, provision must be made for the rapid filling up of the cuts in exceptionally wet seasons.

A good proportion between depth and width of drain is of considerable importance, but it is not often possible to secure an approximation to a proportion of 1 to 2. In ascertaining the required cross-sectional area we may get a drain which is either too wide or too narrow to give a good proportion. If the drain has to discharge into a tideway, the higher the outfall cill is above low water the flatter will be the gradient and the longer will be the period of discharge. We may have to choose between a shallow and wide drain with a high outfall and a long discharge period, and a deeper and narrower drain with a better gradient and a shorter discharge period. A better sectional area and velocity will be secured in the latter case, and this might perhaps offset any disadvantage due to a shorter discharge. There may, too, be a smaller tendency for the sluice to get " landed up " with silt. Outfall sluices near, at, or below low water may usually be depended upon to remain free from silting owing to the flushing power of the land water coming down a steeply inclined drain. Preferably, the outfall sluice of a main drain should discharge into a concave bend of the artery, where the water is likely to be deeper than at other parts.

Now, in discussing dimensions for the arterial outfall channel, the factor of time was considered in relation to tidal conditions. If, therefore, the low-level system is below the level of high water of mean tides, it will be necessary to ascertain the period during which the low-level water can flow out into the tideway whether that be part of the river channel or along the coast.

It was assumed in the case of the arterial outfall conditions that the tidal flow occurred during five hours and the ebb during seven hours, and that the fluvial water might be held up for ten hours a day, i.e., during the whole of the flood period. It may be convenient to adopt the same proportions for our present problem.

If the low-level water discharges into a tideway, it will be able to flow during some part of the flood, viz., that period which is occupied by the tidal water in rising from the dead low water to the level of the outfall sluice. On the other hand, its flow will be stopped during that part of the ebb which is occupied by the fall from high water to sluice level.

The sluices will not close entirely until the outside water level counterheads the inside water level, so we may assume that under ordinary conditions some discharge will take place after the rising tide has overtopped the cill level and again before the falling tide has dropped to cill level. If we assume that effective discharge will cease at one third the depth of the sluices above the cill, that that point is 4 feet above mean low water, and that the vertical range of mean tides at the sluices is 14 feet, the sluices will remain open for discharge on a rising tide during 1·3 hours and on a falling tide during 2 hours. Adding these periods for a single tide we obtain 3·3, or for the two daily tides 6·6 as the daily "tide-open" period. During the remainder of the day the sluices would be tide-locked.

We have therefore to arrange that the discharge capacity of our main drain should be equal to its full daily discharge in six hours and thirty-six minutes.

If we suppose that catchwater drains will be used to divert the water which would otherwise have to pass by the mains through the level, we may assume that five times the daily average run-off for the wettest period is all that need be provided for. In a level of, say, 5,000 acres, we should provide for a daily run-off equal to 1 per cent. of the annual rainfall due to the area, which at 32 inches per annum would be 5,760,000 cubic feet per day of 6·6 hours.

The rate of discharge will be, therefore :—

$$\frac{5,760,000}{6{\cdot}6 \times 60 \times 60} = 243 \text{ cubic feet or } 6\tfrac{3}{4} \text{ tons per second.}$$

Suppose the main drain to be of comparatively short

length, say 2 or 3 miles, with the feeding drains falling into it at intervals of 50 to 60 chains and smaller drains falling into the feeders every 10 chains or so, the sectional area of the main may be kept uniform throughout the length; but if it taps an area of great length with, say, little width at the top end and great width at the bottom end, the feeders and smaller drains farthest from the point of discharge would be shorter than those nearer the outfall, and for that reason the main might taper in plan from full width at outfall to whatever would suffice to conduct the water from the farthest points in its line.

The feeding drains, of which there must of course be a considerable number, may be of any convenient width, but a mean width equal to twice the depth will afford the best section. The combined areas of the feeders had better be much greater than the area of the main, as the gradients of some of them are likely to be very flat, besides which their smaller individual sections will give a higher ratio of resistance due to friction, which in the case of small drains is in appreciable factor being as high as 40 per cent. of the volume for drains discharging low volumes.

The gradients of the feeding drains should be the best obtainable, regard being had to the lay-out of the level for efficient drainage, but it will not be necessary as a rule to spoil the shape of the lands bounded by the drains in order to get the best natural falls. Whilst an eighth of an inch to a mile will cause sensible movement in water, anything less than

1 inch would be practically useless for a gravitation drain. Gradients as low as 1½ to 3 inches to a mile are not uncommon in the Fens. Both the Middle Level Drain and the main drain through Deeping Fen have a superficial gradient of about 1½ inches to a mile.

The batter to be given to the sides of the drains will depend to a large degree upon the nature of the soil cut through, but it is best in most instances to make the slopes as gentle as is consistent with other factors. Storage capacity is thereby gained, and this is no small consideration during exceptionally wet spells, when, as in the case supposed, the low-level water is tide-locked for a large part of each day. Slopes should not, however, be cut to too great a batter, as land is thereby wasted.

In sand, slopes of 2½ to 1, or 3 to 1 are reasonable. Alluvial soils, such as is mostly found in marshlands, will stand up to 1 to 1. Clay will do with ¾ or ½ to 1, whilst peat needs hardly any batter. Hundreds of miles of main and feeding drains in the Fen country have been cut with practically sheer sides and they stand up perfectly.

In some soils, especially those of a boggy nature, the bottom of the drains will swell up into the cut almost as soon as it is made. This was a very noticeable feature in cutting some large drains across Fenn's Moss, in Flintshire, whilst peat moss was being taken for horse litter during the war. Drains of 5 or 6 feet depth almost disappeared in a night owing to the upward thrust of the water in the flanking bog. It was a very practical and a very inconvenient illustration of hydrostatic laws operating upon masses of soil having somewhat the consistency of jelly. If soil of this character has to be dealt with, the excavated earth should be removed from the vicinity of the drain, so that its weight shall not assist the water in forcing up the beds.

In addition to the provision of a suitable sluice at the outfall of the main drain for the exclusion of tidal water, it may be desirable to fit cloughs at the outfall ends of the feeders, or some of them, in order that at tide-locked periods in the main, a heavy flush of water from one part of the level may not overflow from the main into the feeders at another part.

CHAPTER XIII

MAINTENANCE OF THE LOW-LEVEL SYSTEM

GRAVITY is the motive power which causes water to flow. Being entirely free, each molecule of water which has a slightly higher elevation than other molecules will tend to move downward. Thus motion is maintained in channels having very low gradients. At the surface and in a central position the molecules have the freest motion, and will therefore move faster than those nearer the sides and bed of the channel where frictional resistance is greater. But between the free surface motion at the centre of the stream and the more restricted motion of other parts of the mass, there is an average motion which resolves itself into a mean velocity, sometimes taken as 84 per cent. of that of the surface at the centre. If the sides or the bed of the channel are irregular, the sectional area of the mass of moving water is constantly undergoing fluctuation, at one moment deepening and narrowing, at another broadening and shallowing. When these fluctuations occur the centre of gravity of the mass is thrown suddenly and violently out of its path, and depressions in the bed and concavities in the banks are deepened or widened as a consequence.

An accidental fall of earth, an ingrowing bush, a mass of weeds or any other influence which would tend to deflect the path of the centre of gravity of the moving mass, must necessarily prejudice the discharging capacity of a drain. Any local alteration of the section of the mass of water will affect the velocity upward and downward from the point of alteration.

For this reason, low-level drains, having for the most part fine gradients and consequently low velocities, should receive very special and constant attention. It is useless to enter into calculations as to areas and velocities with the object of finding discharge capacities if the drains which have been formed in accordance with ascertained requirements are allowed to deteriorate. Every drain throughout the system should be constantly examined for faults, and any faults should be promptly repaired. The cost of maintenance may be the merest fraction of the cost of neglect, and provision should be made at the outset with as little hesitation as one makes provision for insurance against fire. The fire may never occur, but the drains will certainly fail of their duty if neglected.

If one would blame some irresponsible individual who dumped earth into a drain until it had lost, say, three-fourths of its capacity, what excuse should be found for the person or authority responsible for maintenance who allowed weeds to grow until the effectiveness of the drain was no greater than with the dumped earth? The cumulative effect of weeds may indeed be greater than that of earth, for that might gradually get washed down and spread over the bed, but weeds are so well anchored that no natural influence will move them. Drains having good falls but choked with weeds may lose their whole power of discharge. The author recalls an instance where a main drain designed to tap 1,200 acres of peatland was so choked with dense weed growths that the water, which stood bank high, was absolutely stagnant, and the land that the drain should have tapped was waterlogged to within 6 inches of the surface. After the weeds had been cut and their roots dragged out, the water in the drain fell 2 feet 9 inches and flowed away at a good pace. During the same year the land, which had hardly been cultivated for thirty years, was sown and produced moderately good crops of oats, potatoes and market vegetables.

Long-handled scythes are effective weed-cutters, but they are useless for removing roots. A useful implement for preventing the propagation of weeds or cutting at weed roots is a reversible drag which can traverse the bottom of the drain in either direction. It is mounted on two large central wheels and has two small wheels for leading and trailing which are pivoted to the ends of adjustable arms on which curved knives or cutters are fixed. As the drag is drawn along the bottom of the drain, the knife on the forward arm is brought into cutting position just below bed level and cuts into the bottom and through the roots of any weeds which may have established themselves. For the removal of well-established weed roots, however, digging only is fully effective.

Weeds should not be allowed to grow in drains, but if they appear they should be kept cut down to root level until the roots can be conveniently removed. Weed cutting or "roding" should be done at least twice, preferably thrice a year.

Access to fields across drains is sometimes provided with little or no regard to the efficiency of the drain. A pipe may be laid in the bottom of a drain having several times the area of the pipe and the rest of the space filled in with earth to form a cart-road across the drain. An important drain of about $1\frac{1}{4}$ miles in length and about 16 square feet area in South Lincolnshire is crossed by seventeen such roads under which the largest culvert has an area of $7\frac{1}{2}$ square feet! Those who exercise authority for the maintenance of drainage channels should insist that full-way bridgesonly should be used for crossing drains.

Where cloughs are provided, they should have waterways at least equal to the drains they are intended to discharge. This may seem too obvious a thing to need mention, but neglect of obvious needs is not the least among the causes of trouble in many drainage systems. The edges and corners of wooden cloughs should be banded and gusseted with hoop or sheet iron to prevent their being gnawed by rodents. Leakages through cloughs, caused by rats, are not uncommon.

All drains which traverse pasture lands should be fenced against cattle, and drinking pools should be provided where necessary.

On no account whatever should "stanks," designed to hold up water for cattle-drinking or sheep-washing purposes, be allowed. They are usually erected during dry weather periods, often with the virtuous intention of removing them when the immediate need has passed, but experience goes to show that they are seldom taken up until after they have caused damage either by the flooding of the lands above them or by causing siltation in the upper part of the drain.

CHAPTER XIV

DRAINAGE BY PUMPING

IN very low-lying land, either near the coast or further inland where the arterial channels bringing their water down to the sea are embanked across the levels, it may be impossible to discharge the low-level water otherwise than by pumping it over the embankments by which the level is protected from external water. In other instances, discharge by gravitation can be obtained only when the outside water level falls to or below that of the drains.

There are comparatively few cases in which the whole of the water must be pumped, but there are great areas, especially in the Fens, where dependence upon gravitation alone would be fatal.

In arranging a system which is to be served by gravitation and pumping, it is desirable to make the mains larger and give their beds a steeper inclination than would be otherwise necessary. Although the steeper inclination may somewhat reduce the time during which they could discharge by gravitation owing to the lower level at which the sluice must be placed, it must be of decided advantage during very wet periods when the sluice is closed and the pumps are at work. A "pumping" or "engine" drain with a very low gradient may fail to bring water down as fast as the pumps can deal with it, so rendering the latter temporarily idle. In a notable instance in Yorkshire a set of powerful pumps can dry the engine drain in four hours, whilst a few miles back the main and its feeders may be bank full of water. The engine drain naturally fills up again, but meanwhile the pumps are idle and valuable time is lost. It may be desirable in some cases to widen out the lower end of the engine drain so as to form a pumping reservoir.

The early engineers who designed the pumping drainage of the Fens had little choice of kinds of pumps, and in nearly every case installed scoop wheels with highly satisfactory results. The scoop wheel, which consists of a double frame with scoops or floats set at an angle of from 25° to 45° from the radial line, backward in relation to the drain, is set with its lower scoops just clear of the bed of the engine drain. The drain is continued upward in an arc under the wheel to the outfall point where there is a cill over which the water scooped out of the drain is discharged. The sides of the wheel-pit are just clear of the sides of the wheel, so that very little of the water actually lifted escapes laterally. The scoop wheel which lifts part of the water from the Littleport and Downham Drainage District into the Hundred Foot River at Downham is 50 feet in diameter, has sixty scoops set at a dip of 40° from the radial line and possesses a lift capacity of 17 feet. At full power it can discharge just under 200 tons a minute. In front of the wheel there is a curved adjustable shutter which can be raised well above the level of the water in the outfall channel. It has been found that the adjustment of the height of the crest of the shutter to suit varying outside conditions adds appreciably to the efficiency of the engine in driving the wheel. The engine is of the condensing beam type with cylinders of 43½ inches diameter and 8 feet stroke. There are three Lancashire boilers each 7 feet in diameter and 24 feet in length. This is probably the most powerful scoop wheel plant in England, and may possibly represent something like the maximum desirable for Fen conditions, as the weight of the plant is very great. The outfall sluice doors in front of scoop wheels are sometimes arranged as two or more sets of superimposed leaves, a lower set being closed against low heads of outside water whilst an upper set may remain open, or the whole of the sets may close against high outside heads. In this way the fall of water from the wheel into the outfall channel is eased, and splashing, which might give rise to trouble from ice in winter time, is to some extent avoided.

Apart from other possible defects of scoop wheels, one which may have to be provided against is the sinkage of the bed of the drains as part of a general subsidence due to the abstraction of water from the soil. If that occurs, the space between the bed of the drain and the ends of the scoops widens and the surface line of the water sinks so that the dip of the scoops is lessened and lifting efficiency reduced. It is necessary then to lengthen the scoops, so increasing the load against the engine or to lower the wheel bodily. In either case considerable expense is incurred as neither operation can be carried out without modification of other parts of the plant and of the buildings containing it.

In a large number of instances scoop wheels have been replaced by centrifugal pumps, mostly steam-driven. Some however are driven by suction gas and others by oil engines. At Pode Hole, Deeping Fen, the two scoop wheels have been supplemented by powerful centrifugal pumps driven by a Diesel engine capable of raising about 110 tons per minute against a 7 feet 6 inches lift, whilst at Southery, the new centrifugal pumps are actuated by suction gas plant. In both cases the installations are said to be highly efficient and more economical in working than with steam.

The installation at Southery is of 250 effective horse-power driving one 36 inch centrifugal pump against a maximum lift of 24 feet from the Methwold and Feltwell Fens engine drain into the Ten Mile River. The area drained by the pump is about 10,000 acres.

The great advantage of the centrifugal pump (which is, after all, only an enclosed modification of the scoop wheel) is that it adjusts itself more readily than the wheel to differential lifts. If the drain sinks below or the outside water rises above normal level, the submerged suction and delivery pipes are not deprived of efficiency to lift and discharge the water: all that happens is that the load on the engine may be varied with the lift, but as the engines are usually designed to be well "on top " of the maximum load this is a small matter.

The question of fuel needs careful consideration before the type of plant is decided upon. Steam plant cannot be run without coal, and prices and means of access to the pumping station may be factors of some weight. On the other hand, steam plant has passed its reliability test by generations of experience, whereas some of the more modern types of plant have yet to prove their reputation. Certain classes of accidents happen with suction gas and oil plants which do not happen with steam engines and boilers, and it is probable that the latter will stand more "monkeying" than the former. This is a factor of some importance if highly skilled labour cannot be always obtained.

In cases where steam plant might be preferred, it should be carefully considered whether the water is suitable for the boilers. Water may contain lime or iron or acid which would cause deposit on or pitting in the shells and tubes and on the plates. In the case of calcareous deposit, higher cost for coal with reduced efficiency is the result. In the case of pitting, heavy depreciation and some risk of accident has to be faced.

It would be prudent in any case to have the water analysed by some authority recognized by steam users, and in every case where boilers are used to insure them with a reputable boiler insurance company. Perhaps the most valuable part of boiler insurance is that the companies make periodical inspections of the plant for their own satisfaction and security and send copies of their reports to the users.

In average seasons, gravitation and pumping systems usually discharge by simple run-off during eight or nine months in a year, the remainder of the duty being discharged by the pumps. The periods are sometimes very unequally divided into days or weeks of one or the other, but experience seems to show that fuel and oil for, say, five months will more than suffice for the year's consumption. The pumping periods are naturally longer in winter than in summer, but the capacity of the pumping plant should be such that it could cope with the whole of the year's volume if required. For this purpose it may be worth consideration whether the plant should not be duplicated or that there should be, if not a pair of engines and a pair of pumps, one engine driving either one or two pumps as may be necessary.

In all cases where pumps are used, weed screens should be fitted across the drain above the pump well or suction pit, as, although small masses of weed will generally go through, there is always a risk that something may get into the pumps which would either choke them or break the vanes.

All pumping plants should be periodically overhauled by the makers. No matter how good a man is in charge, he may miss detection or think little of a wheeze or a clank in the running machinery which might mean breakdown at a critical period of the year when the plant was required to go " all out " to keep floods down. Contracts for new plants might reasonably include provisions for an overhaul every five years after the maintenance period.

The capacity of the pumping plant and the power of the engine or engines to work it depend upon the weight of water to be discharged in a given time and on the height of the " lift."

As the lift is usually variable with day to day conditions, the maximum lift should be provided for. The total lift is the difference between the lowest surface level of the water in the drain and the highest surface level of the water in the outside channel.

Suppose it were necessary on occasion to discharge the whole of the water from the low-level area imagined in Chapter XII, we should have to provide power to raise and discharge 5,760,000 cubic feet or, say, 160,000 tons per day. If, as sometimes happens, the pumps were required to be kept running during the full twenty-four hours, the rate of discharge would be

$$\frac{160,000}{24 \times 60} = 111 \text{ tons a minute.}$$

Assuming a lift of from 8 to 10 feet, two 30 inch centrifugal pumps each driven by a 60 B.H.P. engine would more than suffice for the maximum discharge.

The advantages of duplicating pumping plant are (*a*) that economies in working are effected during periods of light duty when one set only may be needed, and (*b*) that in the event of a breakdown one set can be kept running while the other set is undergoing repair.

CHAPTER XV

FIELD DRAINAGE

Ditches

THE modern tendency to use power plant instead of horses for ploughing, harrowing, drilling, etc., is likely to open up in the near future several new questions in connection with the drainage of cultivable lands. In the past, the tendency has been rather to divide farms into fields of convenient size for working by horse-traction, each such field having its own boundary hedges and ditches. Now, however, there is a growing tendency to grub up hedges, fill in ditches, and turn two, three or more fields into one, with the consequence that the total area loses some of the open channels by which it was formerly drained.

If, as is probable in the case of well-farmed lands, tile drains of adequate dimensions have been provided to carry off the water which formerly flowed by the ditches before they were filled in, the general balance of advantage might lie with the new arrangement, as the trouble and expense of keeping the ditches properly "bottomed-out" and free from rubbish would be saved, whilst the drains would not only be likely to draw from a wider area than the ditches but would be freer from the action of frost.

It is quite a nice question whether all ditches of say less than 4 feet width should not be piped and filled in. The first cost might be considerable, but the cost of upkeep and maintenance of the watercourse would practically disappear, whilst the effectiveness of the drainage would probably be much enhanced.

Where it exists, the field ditch should be so maintained as to conform to the general principles which have been laid down for other portions of the arterial system. The necessity of as good a gradient as may be obtainable is the same, but there is an even higher need of depth than in the case of the larger channels, because the ditches or some of them form the outfall channels for the mains of underdrainage systems.

It has been previously recommended that wherever possible, upland and low-level water should be kept apart, but it is often found in practice that field ditches are essential links in a long chain of channels by which water from the uplands is carried down, often by very devious routes, into the main arteries. If they are not of sufficient depth to conduct that water past the lands of the lower levels, the latter are liable to suffer from flooding by upland water. In any case, that water might rise to a sufficient height in the ditches to seal the ends of any tile drains which should discharge into them or even to flow up those drains. Where, therefore, upland water is conducted by a ditch, that ditch should be more than ordinarily deep. It may be pointed out again that, with any given gradient, the velocity of a stream varies as the square root of its depth. If, therefore, upland-water ditches are kept at a good depth the water from the higher levels and tile drains will have a better chance of getting away in good time to allow the slower moving water from the low-level ditches to discharge freely into them.

Field ditches which discharge into upland-water ditches need nor necessarily be so deep on the latter, but they should be of sufficient depth to ensure that the normal level of their water should be well below the outfall ends of any tile drains which may discharge into them. The outfall ends of the ditches themselves should be sloped off, say for 20 to 30 yards back from the upland-water ditch, so that their water has not to make a sudden vertical fall into the main ditch, which might otherwise become liable to be blocked up by masses of earth washed in from the end of the higher-level ditch.

Every ditch which falls into another ditch or into any other channel should have its outfall end curved at easy radius into the other, so that the two streams may not unnecessarily conflict to the detriment of the flow of each.

No general rule can be laid down for the widths and depths of field ditches, as so much depends upon their various duties in relation to size of field, nature of soil, rainfall, slope, etc., but it may be broadly stated that the general average dimensions of field ditches in England and Wales are too small for safety. The ditches are for the most part no larger than their original dimensions, which were probably determined before underdrainage became as general as it is now.

Underdrains cannot, of course, empty from the soil more water than comes into it from the clouds, but they can and do empty that water far more rapidly and to a greater depth and volume than would the undrained soil itself. Field ditches which receive the discharges of underdrains should be therefore dimensioned to areas which would be adequate to the run-off of about three times the volume that would be likely to come into them in the same time from the same area of land if that land were not underdrained.

Suppose we were dealing with an underdrained area of 100 acres of moderately flat land divided into fields by a main and three minor ditches which had to carry away the water due to the 100 acres plus that due to 900 acres of land outside and at a higher level than the 100 acres. If the rainfall of the district were, say, 32 inches per annum, the main ditch should have an area equal to the discharge of 1 per cent. of the rainfall due to the full thousand acres, or, say, 13 cubic feet per second, and each of the minor ditches should have areas equal to the discharge of one-third the run-off due in the same proportion to one hundred acres.

The shape of a ditch is of some importance, but it

is sometimes impossible to give to the slope nearest the hedge the necessary amount of batter. It might be as well for several reasons not to attempt to cut back too much of the side of a ditch on the hedge slope, one reason being that an uncovering of rootlets might encourage an extension of the hedge growth into the channel of the ditch. On the other side, however, the slope should be as a rule not less than one horizontal to one vertical measured from the finished bed of the ditch after its width and slope have been improved to ascertained requirements.

Where ditches traverse or skirt pasture fields they should as a rule be fenced against cattle, and drinking pools should be provided as recommended for the smaller of the main channels, as otherwise considerable damage to their banks and beds might be caused by cattle when watering or sheltering under the hedges during hot weather.

Every means should be taken to keep ditches clear of weeds or other obstructions. Complaints are often heard from farmers that it is useless for them to keep their own watercourses open if those below them are choked up. This is largely true, but it may be suggested that, failing more neighbourly means, one way of inducing attention to possibly unsatisfactory condition of ditches at a lower level is for the farmer up above to send his water down to the point of blockage and await developments. In any case there is a legal remedy against blockage under Section 14 of the Land Drainage Act, 1847.

UNDERDRAINAGE

The practice of underdrainage is already so prevalent that few words are needed to recommend it. The methods also are so widely and so well understood that it is perhaps unnecessary to do more than recapitulate them.

It is notorious that the effect of underdrainage on tenacious soils is to assist in breaking them up by contraction following the drying process. Instead of remaining a hard, cold, compact mass which cannot be easily penetrated by air, heat or moisture the soil is rendered open and free to the admission of those sweetening agents and to the fuller advantages to be derived from the deeper application of fertilizers.

The temperature of underdrained soil is appreciably higher than that of undrained soil. Its capacity of absorption of heat is greater and its rate of radiation less in proportion to the depth of the saturation level below the surface.

Underdrainage should usually be done in the early part of the year, preferably in February. After laying, the pipes should be lightly covered with a layer of soil and the trenches left open, say, for a month or six weeks to allow the soil between the trenches to break up somewhat and form natural channels towards the drains. Later, the trenches may be loosely filled in. If the weather should be wet, it is better to defer the commencement of the work, as trampling the earth along the lines of the intended drains may do harm.

The depth at which the pipes should be laid will naturally depend upon the nature of the soil and upon the possibility of good outfalls for the mains.

If the ditches will not permit of a lower outfall than 2 or 3 feet below the general level of the land, that must of course fix the maximum depth, but in ordinarily tenacious soils it is generally better to go deeper than 3 feet. Probably 3 feet 6 inches is a good all-round depth in average soils, although Professor H. Kinglake, of Wisconsin, advises a minimum depth of 4 feet.

Drains should always be laid so as to run with the fall of the land. This has not always been the practice, but experience has proved the advantage of this course. The main or mains should as a rule take the lowest levels, but it may be sometimes more convenient to place them centrally to the fields to be drained despite that not being the lowest line of surface.

The inclination of the main towards the outfall need not be great: indeed some long mains which have had to be laid dead level have acted very well, but in these cases the diameters were not less than 6 inches. The better the inclination the smaller need be the diameter, but in no case should a main have a less diameter than 4 inches.

The outfall ends of the mains should be embedded in concrete and led over a concrete or stone cill into a catchpit built clear of the alignment of the outfall ditch. The catchpit should be of sufficient capacity to contain, say, three months' accumulation of sand or silt from the drain. It is prudent in most cases to protect the ends of the mains by means either of a wire cap or a little clough so as to prevent the entry of vermin.

The laterals, which should be led into the mains at a slight angle towards the outfall, should never be of less than 2½ inches diameter, and had better be 3 inches if the mains are of 5 or 6 inches. Their distance apart will depend upon depth and the nature of the soil, but supposing they are not less than 3 feet deep the distances may be as under :—

In sandy soil . . .	60 to 75 feet.
Sand with clay . .	30 ,, 50 ,,
Heavy loam . . .	25 ,, 30 ,,
Stiff clay	15 ,, 20 ,,

The inclination of lateral drains towards the mains should be not less than 1 foot in 10 chains.

As a rule, collars should be used. They do not prevent the admission of water to the drains, and are extremely useful in preventing short lengths dropping out of alignment due to local movements of earth.

An example of the drainage by pipes of about 90 acres of moderately flat land in soil of average texture was as under :—

Field Drainage

	Number.	Length.	Diameter.
		Feet.	Inches.
Mains	1	1,500	6
		1,080	4
	1	1,000	7
		1,200	6
		600	5
		157	4
Secondary	1	250	5
Laterals.	17	6,380	4
		3,860	3

Appendix I

HYDRAULIC MEMORANDA

Cubic feet × 6·232, say $6\frac{1}{4}$ = gallons.
Tons × 224 = gallons.
Tons × 35·97, say 36 = cubic feet.
Cubic feet of water × ·0278 = tons.
Gallons of water × ·004464 = tons.
One cubic foot of fresh water = 62·4 say, $62\frac{1}{2}$ lbs.
One cubic foot of sea water = 64·11 lbs.
One gallon of fresh water = 10 lbs.
One gallon of sea water = 10·27 lbs.
One inch of rain = 3640 cubic feet per acre.
One inch of rain = 101 tons per acre.
Head in feet × ·434 = pressure in lbs. per square inch.
Pressure in lbs. per square inch × 2·3 = head in feet.
Pressure in lbs. per square foot = head in feet × 62·4.

VELOCITIES OF STREAMS

Mean velocity $= (S + 0{\cdot}5) - \sqrt{S}$ (Molesworth.)

" " $\left\{\begin{array}{l} = \cdot 815\ S \text{ for smaller channels} \\ = \cdot 835\ S \text{ for larger channels} \end{array}\right\}$ (Neville.)

where S = surface velocity in inches per second at centre of stream.

$$V = \sqrt{R \times 2\ F} \times C$$

where V = mean velocity in feet per second. R = hydraulic mean radius. F = fall in feet per mile and C = constant for friction. R is found by dividing the area of the channel in square feet by the length in feet of its wetted perimeter. C varies from ·9 for average river channels to ·6 for small drains.

For approximations, V = surface velocity at centre × ·84.

DISCHARGE BY OPEN CHANNELS

$$D = V \times A.$$

Where D = discharge in cubic feet per second : V = mean velocity of stream in feet per second, and A = area of channel in square feet.

DISCHARGE OVER WEIRS

$$C = 214 \sqrt{h^3}.$$

Where C = cubic feet per minute per foot width, and h = head in feet from cill to still surface.

When the water passes the point where the constant head begins to deflect with an appreciable initial velocity

$$V = \text{feet per second, } C = 214 \sqrt{h^3 + {\cdot}035\, v^2 h^2}.$$

(Santo Crimp's formula has the constant 195 instead of 214 in each case.)

(Adams.)

FOR SMALL WEIRS

$$G = 2L \sqrt{D^3}.$$

Where G = gallons discharged per minute.
L = length of weir or notch in inches.
D = depth of head in inches.

Approximate rule :—

If H = height of flow on edge of rule over square notch or edge of horizontal weir, and C = cubic feet per minute per foot of width,

H				C
H = 1	inch,	then C	=	5·10.
$1\frac{1}{4}$	,,	,,	=	7·14.
$1\frac{1}{2}$	,,	,,	=	9·23.
$1\frac{3}{4}$	,,	,,	=	11·78.
2	,,	,,	=	14·43.

(Hawksley.)

DISCHARGE THROUGH GATE SLUICES

$$D = W \times H \times 8 \sqrt{C} \times \cdot 75 \times 60.$$

Where D = discharge in cubic feet per minute ; W = width of opening ; H = height of opening above cill in feet, and C = height from centre of opening to surface of water.

NOTE :—For small drains of low initial velocity, any addition which might be otherwise made for speed of approach would be cancelled by friction at the sluice.

DISCHARGE THROUGH CLOUGHS

If counterbalanced, same rule as above + ·05 to ·1.
If not counterbalanced ,, ,, − ·05 to ·1.

CENTRIFUGAL PUMPS

Size of Pump and diameter of Pipes.	Nominal H.P. of Engine for each foot of vertical height from level of water to top of delivery bend.	Maximum quantity of water raised per minute.
		Gallons.
3	·045	150
4	·078	260
5	·121	400
6	·175	580
7	·242	800
8	·303	1,000
10	·484	1,600
12	·700	2,300
13	·818	2,700
16	1·242	4,100
18	1·606	5,300
20	1·970	6,500
24	2·848	9,400

(*Engineers' Year Book.*)

Appendix I

WINDMILL PUMPS

Allowing for 8 hours' work per day and a breeze of 14 miles per hour giving a pressure of 1 lb. per square foot of sail area.

Diameter of Sail.	Horse-power.
10	0·25
12	0·50
16	1·00
20	1·75
25	2·50
30	4·00
35	6·00
40	8·00

(Adams.)

For drainage purposes an 8-foot mill will raise 500 to 600 gallons per hour, and a 12-foot mill 1,200 to 1,400 gallons per hour.

(Maclellan.)

Appendix II

FLOODS AND WATERLOGGED LAND: THE LAND DRAINAGE ACT, 1918 *

1. THE NEED for ARTERIAL DRAINAGE.—There are estimated to be in England and Wales something like a million acres which, by the improvement of arterial drainage, might be either brought into arable cultivation or greatly increased in value as grass land. In view of the urgent need at present existing, and likely to continue to exist for some years at least, of utilizing for the purpose of food production every available acre of land, this brief summary of the changes made and facilities afforded by the new Land Drainage Act has been prepared for the information of local authorities and of all persons interested in the land.

2. PREVIOUS DIFFICULTIES IN DEALING WITH THE MATTER.—Private efforts, having in view the prevention of floods and the more efficient drainage of agricultural land, have often been attended with little success, as the endeavours of energetic owners and tenants have been neutralized by the failure of others to carry out work essential to proper drainage, and difficulties have arisen in securing combined action by the whole of those concerned. These difficulties have been especially apparent where the owners and occupiers of the land have amounted to any considerable number.

In many places Commissions of Sewers have been established for centuries; in others, drainage authorities have been constituted under local Acts; and a number

* Food Production Leaflet No. 56.

of Drainage Boards have been set up under the Land Drainage Act, 1861. The total area dealt with is, however, small compared with the large area of floodable and waterlogged land capable of improvement in the country. In many instances also the drainage districts have been formed with a view to isolated areas and without any provision for co-ordination between the drainage authorities exercising jurisdiction in the same river basin.

In the past, there have been two chief obstacles to the setting up of Drainage Boards. First, it was necessary, before the Board of Agriculture and Fisheries could set up a Drainage Board for any area, that a petition should be received by them from the owners of not less than one-tenth part of the acreage affected. Consequently, where the owners of any area requiring drainage were apathetic in the matter, neither the Board of Agriculture and Fisheries nor any other body could initiate proceedings. Again, in the event of a Provisional Order being drafted by the Board the assent of the owners of two-thirds of the area was required before any further step could be taken, and the trouble and expense involved in obtaining consent in cases where many owners were concerned often discouraged persons who would otherwise have initiated proceedings.

A further impediment to speedy procedure under the Act of 1861 was the requirement that any Order made by the Board setting up a Drainage Board, even in those cases where there was no opposition, should be inoperative until confirmed by Parliament.

3. Difficulties Removed by the Act of 1918.—The Land Drainage Act, 1918, is intended to facilitate the establishment of Drainage Boards, to render possible a revision of drainage areas so as to suit modern conditions, and to assist in various other ways the renewal and extension of arterial drainage.

4. Establishment of Drainage Boards.—Part I. of the new Act (Sections 1 and 2) considerably modifies procedure for these purposes. An Order constituting a separate drainage district may now be framed by the

Board on receipt of a petition from the owners of one-tenth of the proposed area (as formerly), or from the council of any county or county borough in which any part of the land proposed to be affected by the Order is situate, or the Board may themselves initiate proceedings for such an Order. After due notice has been given, copies of the Draft Order deposited, objections considered, and, if necessary, a local inquiry held, the Board may proceed to settle the Order unless within a prescribed period the owners of one-third of the proposed district signify their objection to the making of the Order in which case the Order cannot be made. The Order, when settled, becomes operative after 30 days' notice, unless within that period a memorial against it is presented to the Board, in which case (unless the memorial is withdrawn) the Order requires the confirmation of Parliament.

If the Order comes into force the expenses of obtaining it are, under Section 3, made a first charge on the rates of the district constituted by the Order. If the petitioners do not obtain the Order, they are required to pay the expenses.

5. Alteration of Boundaries.—The boundaries of an existing drainage area may be extended or altered (by a similar procedure) with the consent of the drainage authority for the area, and the petition may emanate from that authority.

The limits of a Commission of Sewers may be defined on the petition of the Commission.

6. Powers to Transfer to County Councils.—Provision is also made (Section 1 (2)), for the transfer, subject to certain conditions, on the petition of a county or county borough council, to such council of the powers, duties, property and obligations of drainage authorities exercising jurisdiction within the counties or county boroughs; such a transfer may also be made to a joint committee of county and county borough councils where the drainage area is within the jurisdiction of more than one council. The expenses incurred by a council as the drainage authority are to be defrayed under the trans-

ferred powers, and not out of the council's rates or funds.

The expression " drainage authority " is defined in Section 13 and includes Commissions of Sewers, Drainage Boards, and any body of persons authorized by a Local Act or Award to make or maintain works for the drainage of agricultural land.

7. Increase of Rating Powers: Limit of Rates.—In many instances a drainage authority is hampered in the execution of necessary works by a limit of rates which is inconsistent with modern conditions or by some other disabling or inadequate provision; to meet such cases the Act empowers the Board to confer upon a drainage authority additional powers of levying rates and borrowing, and of altering or supplementing the provisions of any local Act or award from which its powers are derived, where this is found necessary or expedient for the purpose of effective drainage (Section 1 (1)).

The petition for the Order may be presented by the drainage authority, or by the council of any county or county borough in which any part of the drainage area is situate.

8. Other Provisions as to Rating.—Section 4 removes any doubt as to the power of a Commission of Sewers, or a Drainage Board constituted under the Land Drainage Acts, to levy rates on the basis of acreage, and validates rates levied on that basis whether before or after the passing of the Act; but does not prohibit rating on the basis of annual value. The same Section enables an Order to provide for differential rating of a part of a drainage area or for total or partial exemption of buildings, railways, canals, inland navigation or any other special class of land.

9. Contributions by Urban and Rural Authorities.—Section 5 empowers local authorities, with the concurrence of the Local Government Board, to contribute to the expenses of drainage authorities where drainage works are desirable in the interests of the public health or for the protection or better enjoyment of highways.

10. COMBINATION OF DRAINAGE AUTHORITIES.—Under Section 6, any drainage authority can make arrangements with the drainage authority of an adjoining area for the execution of works in the latter area on such terms of payment or otherwise as may be agreed.

11. NAVIGATIONS : POWER TO TRANSFER TO DRAINAGE AUTHORITIES.—Section 7 provides under certain conditions for the entry of drainage authorities and navigation authorities into arrangements for the execution of necessary drainage works ; and for the transfer to a drainage authority of the whole or any part of the undertaking of a navigation authority. This power may be of value in cases where the remains of obsolete navigation works form an obstacle to an effective drainage scheme.

12. OUTFALLS OUTSIDE DRAINAGE AREAS.—Section 8 enables drainage authorities to execute works outside their district under the same procedure as exists under the Land Drainage Act, 1847, and Part III. of the Land Drainage Act, 1861, for enabling persons interested in land to secure outfalls for their drains.

13. ANNUAL RETURNS.—Section 9 requires every drainage authority to send to the Board of Agriculture and Fisheries annually, before a date which will be fixed by the Board, a report of their proceedings during the previous year. The form of report will be prescribed by Regulation.

14. POWER TO INVEST ON SECURITY OF RATES.—Section 12 authorizes owners of land in a drainage area, who have power to invest money on real security, to invest money on a first mortgage of the drainage rates leviable in the area.

15. NEW POWERS CONFERRED UPON THE BOARD.—Part II. of the new Act confers on the Board of Agriculture and Fisheries powers of considerable importance to secure the due performance of duties and obligations with regard to arterial drainage, and to arrange for the arterial drainage of small areas ; these powers are summarised in the following paragraphs.

16. POWER TO ENFORCE CARRYING OUT OF DUTIES AND LIABILITIES.—Under Section 15 of the Sewers Act,

1833, where a person or body liable to maintain works affecting drainage has failed to do so, an officer appointed by a Court of Sewers is empowered to execute any needful repairs and recover the expenses incurred from the person or body liable. This power may now be exercised under Section 15 (1) of the new Act by any officer appointed by and acting on behalf of the Board of Agriculture.

Section 15 (2) empowers the Board to exercise drainage powers conferred by any general or local Act or any Order or Award or by any Commission of Sewers, which are not being exercised or are being insufficiently exercised. This Sub-section enables the Board of Agriculture, if any drainage authority fails to maintain efficient drainage, to carry out the necessary work in place of the authority and to recoup their expenditure by the exercise of the authority's rating and borrowing powers. It also enables the Board to enforce the draining provisions of Inclosure Awards.

17. Drainage Schemes for Small Areas.—In Section 16 provision is made for dealing with the drainage of areas of land capable of improvement which cannot be conveniently dealt with under Part I. of the Act. Where the Board of Agriculture are of opinion that any such area is capable of improvement by drainage works, and that the expenses of executing and maintaining the works will not exceed the increase of the value of the land arising therefrom, they may prepare a draft scheme detailing the area to be improved, the proposed works, the estimated cost of their execution, the maximum amount recoverable by the Board in respect of such cases (not to exceed £5 per acre, or £5,000 in all), and the manner in which the expenses of executing and maintaining the works are to be apportioned amongst the lands in the area. The draft scheme is to be deposited for inspection, and notices given to the owners and occupiers of land in the area, and to other bodies and persons interested, so that objections may be made and considered before the scheme is finally settled. For the purpose of executing and maintaining these works, the Board have, within the area concerned, all

the powers of a Drainage Board, and the expenses of execution (up to the maximum stated in the scheme) and of maintenance are recoverable by the Board in a summary manner, subject to the proviso that, if an owner so requires, the sum payable by him may be payable by instalments in the same manner as in the case of a private improvement rate for private improvement expenses incurred by a Local Authority under the Public Health Act, 1875.

18. DELEGATION OF POWERS.—The Board of Agriculture have power under Section 17 to delegate any of their powers under Part II. of the Act to bodies constituted in accordance with the terms of that Section.

Statutory Rules and Orders, 1918, No. 1605.

DRAINAGE AND IMPROVEMENT OF LAND, ENGLAND.

THE LAND DRAINAGE REGULATIONS, 1918, DATED NOVEMBER 20, 1918, MADE BY THE BOARD OF AGRICULTURE AND FISHERIES UNDER THE LAND DRAINAGE ACT, 1918 (8 & 9 GEO. 5, C. 17).

The Board of Agriculture and Fisheries in exercise of the powers conferred on them under the Land Drainage Act, 1918, hereby make the following regulations :—

Section 2, Subss. (4) (5).

1. The period within which an objection to the making of an order may be signified to the Board in the case :—

(*a*) of a Draft Order for the constitution of an area as a separate drainage district for the purposes of Part II. of the Land Drainage Act, 1861, or

(*b*) of a Draft Order for the inclusion in any drainage district of any drainage area or any part of any drainage area, or

(*c*) of a Draft Order for the alteration of the Boundaries of any drainage area, by proprietors of land within the proposed drainage district or of land proposed to be added to or excluded from the drainage area,

shall be one calendar month after the publication of the Draft Order by notice thereof in the *London Gazette*.

Section 9.

2. (1) The date in every year before which a Drainage Authority shall send to the Board of Agriculture and Fisheries a report of their proceedings during the preceding year shall be the first day of April, unless on the application of the Drainage Authority the Board shall fix another date as applicable to such Drainage Authority.

(2) The report shall be in the form set forth in the Schedule to these Regulations and contain such information as is prescribed by that form.

Section 16, Subs. (2).

3. (1) Notice of the making of a draft scheme under section sixteen of the said Act for the improvement of an area and of the place where it can be inspected and of the time within which objections to the scheme may be presented to the Board shall be given in the following manner :—

(*a*) A notice to an owner or occupier of land comprised within the area or to any other person appearing to the Board to be affected by the scheme shall be served on the owner, occupier or other person either personally or by leaving it for him at his last known place of abode or by sending it through the post in a registered letter addressed to him there ; or, where the name and place of abode of the owner or occupier of any land cannot reasonably be ascertained by the Board, a notice to such person may be served by affixing a copy of the notice to some part of the land ;

(*b*) A notice to a navigation authority or other body appearing to the Board to be affected by the scheme shall be served by being sent by registered post addressed to the clerk or secretary of the authority or body at the office of the authority or body or of the clerk or secretary; and

(*c*) A copy of the notice shall be published in a newspaper circulating in the district in which the area is situate.

(2) A notice required to be given to the owner of land comprised within an area shall be sent by registered post—

(*a*) in the case of land under the management of the Commissioners of Woods, to those Commissioners;

(*b*) in the case of land under the management of the Board of Trade, to the Secretary of that Board;

(*c*) in the case of land belonging to the Duchy of Lancaster, to the Chancellor of that Duchy at the Office for the time being of the Duchy; and

(*d*) in the case of land vested in or enjoyed by the Duke of Cornwall or the possessor for the time being of the Duchy of Cornwall, to the Secretary to the Council of that Duchy.

First Schedule, Para. (3).

4. (1) The persons or bodies affected by an Order under the said Act who have an interest sufficient for the presentation of a memorial that the Order shall not become law without confirmation by Parliament shall be such as are prescribed in this regulation.

(A) In the case of an Order for the constitution of an area as a separate drainage district for the purposes of Part II. of the Land Drainage Act, 1861, or of an Order for the alteration of the boundaries of any existing drainage area—

(i) the proprietor of any land proposed to be included in the drainage district intended to be constituted or proposed to be included in or excluded from the existing drainage area ; and

(ii) the drainage authority of the existing drainage area.

(B) In the case of an Order for the definition of the limits of any Commission of Sewers—

(i) the Commission ; and

(ii) the proprietor of any land within the limits of the Commission as defined by the Order.

(C) In the case of an Order conferring on any drainage authority additional powers of levying drainage rates or borrowing or altering or supplementing in any other respect the provisions of any local Act or award—

(i) the drainage authority ; and

(ii) the proprietors of not less than one-tenth part of the drainage area of the drainage authority.

(D) In the case of an Order for the transfer to a council of an administrative county, or county borough, of the powers, duties, property or obligations of a drainage authority—

(i) the drainage authority ; and

(ii) the proprietors of not less than one-tenth part of the drainage area of the drainage authority.

(E) In the case of any Order under the said Act—

(i) the council of any administrative county or county borough in which a drainage area affected by the Order, or the drainage district proposed to be constituted by the Order, or any part of the area or district is situate ; and

(ii) any body or person certified by the Board to be affected by the Order and to have an interest sufficient for the presentation of a memorial.

(2) Where an Order proposes to make any river, canal or inland navigation or any works

belonging thereto liable to the control of a drainage authority, any navigation authority or other body entitled under any Act to navigate or use or to receive tolls or dues in respect of the navigation or use of the river, canal or inland navigation shall be deemed to have an interest sufficient for the presentation of a memorial that the Order shall not become law without confirmation by Parliament.

5. In these Regulations the expression " drainage authority " means any Commission of Sewers, any drainage board constituted under the Land Drainage Act, 1861, or the said Land Drainage Act, 1918, and any body of persons authorized by any local Act or any award made under any such Act to make or maintain works for the drainage of land ; the expression " navigation authority " means any person or body of persons having powers under any Act to work or maintain a canal or other inland navigation ; and the expression " proprietor " means any person defined as a proprietor by section six of the Land Drainage Act, 1861.

6. These Regulations may be cited as the Land Drainage Regulations, 1918.

In witness whereof the Board of Agriculture and Fisheries have hereunto set their Official Seal this twentieth day of November, Nineteen hundred and Eighteen.

F. L. C. FLOUD,
Assistant Secretary.

Appendix II

Schedule.

Form of annual report to the Board of Agriculture and Fisheries by a Drainage Authority of their proceedings during the previous year.

REPORT ON PROCEEDINGS IN THE YEAR 19

1. Name of Drainage Authority. ....
2. New plant installed for pumping or otherwise improving the drainage of the Authority's area. ....
3. Any other works executed for the improvement of drainage. ....
4. Loans raised by the Authority during the year. ....
5. Drainage rate levied during the year, specifying whether on acreage or on annual value; and giving particulars of different rates levied, if different rating is in force. ....
6. (Where a copy of accounts of the Drainage Authority is not furnished with this report) a statement in the following form:—

STATEMENT OF TOTAL RECEIPTS AND EXPENDITURE OF THE AUTHORITY DURING THE YEAR 19

Receipts.	£ s. d.	Expenditure.	£ s. d.
From Loans . .		Interest on Loans .	
From Rates or Taxes . . .		Repayment of Loans.	
From Tolls or Dues . . .		Expenditure on new works	
From other sources . .		Expenditure on improvements of existing works . .	
		Expenditure on maintenance of existing works	
		Salaries and other establishment charges	
		Other expenditure .	

Signature of Chairman ....
Signature of Clerk ....
Address of Clerk..

Date..

Appendix II

On November 19, 1918, a copy of Leaflet 56 was sent to the Clerk of each County Council and each County Borough Council in England and Wales with the following letter :—

THE LAND DRAINAGE ACT, 1918: CIRCULAR LETTER.

SIR,—I am directed by the President of the Board of Agriculture and Fisheries to enclose herewith a copy of a leaflet (F.P. No. 56) summarising briefly the provisions of the Land Drainage Act, 1918.

Owing to a variety of causes, the channels (both natural and artificial) carrying the arterial drainage of agricultural land have in many parts of the country lapsed into such a condition that they are no longer capable of efficiently discharging that function. The experience gained by the Board of Agriculture in the course of carrying out their policy of increased food production, necessary by the pressure of war conditions, has shown that a considerable improvement in arterial drainage is urgently necessary in order that a very large aggregate acreage of potentially good arable and profitable pasture land may not continue to remain derelict or semi-derelict, with a resultant loss of food to the country, and of revenue to the State and to Local Authorities.

The improvements required vary in different districts. Some areas require more or less elaborate schemes involving the expenditure of a considerable amount of money and a large supply of labour, or need the provision of machinery for pumping and other purposes. These cases could not, for obvious reasons, be dealt with during the progress of the War, but in many other instances it was shown that the application of a relatively small amount of labour, rightly directed, would at once set free a considerable acreage for the production of food, and a great deal of good work has been done in this direction by the Agricultural Executive Committees acting on behalf of the Board under the Defence of the Realm Regulations.

Appendix II

Some substantial time may still elapse before schemes can be undertaken which involve the installation of mechanical appliances on an important scale; but there are many, both small and large, which can be carried out by manual labour, so as to effect very substantial improvements. Mr. Prothero is desirous that every effort should be made to maintain the progress that has already been made and to deal with the larger schemes at the earliest opportunity, and for this purpose it is in many cases, where a considerable area is affected and where an efficient authority is not already in existence, a necessary preliminary to any effective action that some authority having complete control of the drainage should be set up for the area.

The Land Drainage Act, 1918, facilitates the establishment of new drainage authorities and the extension of powers of those already established, and provides in various other ways a ready means of improving arterial drainage. The Act also makes it possible for County and County Borough Councils to assist very largely in the matter. Thus under Section 1 (2) the powers and duties of existing drainage authorities may be transferred to them on their application; under Section 2 (2) a Council may petition the Board for an Order under the Act and thus initiate proceedings for the benefit of drainage; and provision is made in Section 10 for joint action by two or more councils when this is necessary or desirable. Consultation with the County or County Borough Councils concerned is provided for, before the making of any draft order by the Board. Part II. of the Act, which provides a means of enforcing upon drainage authorities and private persons the carrying out of their duties and liabilities in this matter, enables the Board to deal with the drainage of areas too small or otherwise unsuitable for the establishment of drainage authorities. The powers of the Board of Agriculture under this part of the Act may be delegated to a body of persons, the majority of whom shall be members of the County or County Borough Councils in the area concerned.

I am directed to ask you to be so good as to invite the attention of your Council to this important matter, and I am to express the Board's confidence that the Council will be willing to co-operate with them in utilizing the provisions of the new Act for the amelioration of drainage conditions in their area by either actually initiating proceedings themselves or by drawing the Board's attention to any case in which it is considered that beneficial action can be undertaken.

I am, etc.,

(Signed) E. M. KONSTAM,

Director of Land Drainage.

WAR EMERGENCY WORKS

As showing what may be sometimes achieved at small cost the following extract from the *Journal* of the Board of Agriculture for January, 1919, may be of interest:—

LAND DRAINAGE: REMARKABLE FIGURES FROM YORKSHIRE

During 1918 and 1917 the subject of improving the main-drainage channels has been taken up with great enthusiasm in Yorkshire among other counties; and remarkable results have been achieved at a comparatively small cost. The low-lying lands around Doncaster and on the north bank of the Humber are provided with drainage systems which have long existed; but many of these were in a state of great neglect when the Agricultural Executives of the East and West Ridings turned their attention to this matter in the spring of 1917.

In the East Riding the cleansing of the Greenoak Goit was completed in 1917, and about 2,000 acres were greatly improved thereby at a cost of £600. Work on the Bellasize Drain was completed in October, 1918, in spite of difficulties caused by the shifting nature of the sandy clay soil. The drain is now said to be working more efficiently than it has done for seventy years past; and an area of approximately 4,000 acres has been greatly benefited at an expense of about £1,200. The water in the Market Weighton Canal (which forms the outlet of the River Foulness) has been substantially lowered by the regulation of the lock gates giving on to the Humber, and the cleansing of the canal is being carried out; the area which will ultimately be benefited by this work extends to about 20,000 acres. The Committee have commenced work upon the clearance of the Howden drainage system.

The following is a brief summary of the principal work carried out by the West Riding Agricultural Executive Committee:—

West Moor and Parks Drains.—Area improved, 3,327 acres; area reclaimed, 700 acres; estimated cost, £1,365.

Tickhill.—Area improved, 2,750 acres; area reclaimed, 200 acres; actual cost, £364 18*s.* 4*d.*

Thorne.—Area improved, 13,000 acres; area reclaimed, 200 acres; estimated cost, £2,700.

Gowdall.—Area improved, 700 acres; estimated cost, £250.

River Don.—Area improved, by clearing a short and much congested reach, 40,000 acres; estimated cost, £500.

Awkley Bridge (River Torne).—Area improved, 2,000 acres; actual cost, £17; arches altered by County Council and other work undertaken by private owners.

Awkley and Blaxton.—Area affected, 2,500 acres; estimated cost, £50.

Doncaster and Balby Car.—Area improved, 300 acres.

Lower Anker Drain.—Area improved, 250 acres; estimated cost, £140.

Tranmoor Drain.—Area improved, 150 acres; estimated cost, £50.

Little Went Drainage.—On representation by the Committee the Little Went has been cleaned out by co-operation of adjoining owners; this is not known to have been done before at any time, and the improvement is considerable.

The Committee and their Chief Executive Officer also undertook with great promptitude the repair of the disastrous breaches in the banks of the Ouse and the Aire which occurred in September, 1918.

The above are given only as examples of the results that can be achieved by manual labour alone without mechanical appliances, such as steam dredgers or pumping engines.

Other counties have not lagged behind ; and similar work has been done (to give only a few instances) in counties so far apart as the North Riding of Yorkshire, Norfolk, Berkshire, Cheshire, Lancashire and Flintshire.

As an instance of the interest and excellent achievement in drainage matters which have marked the activities of Agricultural Executive Committees all over the county, the following review of the work of the Cambridgeshire Committee dated January 30, 1919, deserves particular mention :—

LAND DRAINAGE IN CAMBRIDGESHIRE

That the Cambridgeshire War Agricultural Executive Committee realized the importance of improving the waterways throughout the county at a very early period of its activities is shown by a review of the drainage work carried out by the Committee during 1917 and 1918.

The Committee's opinion was confirmed by the report of the Surveyors who made an inspection of all land in the county in January, 1918, in order to ascertain what further acreage of land could be brought into cultivation. The report showed that several thousand acres of permanent pasture liable to flooding was included in the total acreage of grass land contained in the Agricultural Returns on which the county's quota was fixed. It was also reported that a very large acreage of arable land was waterlogged throughout the winter months so that work was impossible until late in the spring.

In November, 1917, a small prisoner Camp was established at Meldreth, and by August, 1918, the bed of the River Mel was scoured and cleansed, overhanging and unsound trees were removed from the water's edge and the banks were repaired. It was found possible to dam and by-pass the water during the summer months and the accumulation of mud was thrown or wheeled out in barrows. This work was carried out under orders issued on frontage occupiers under the Defence of the Realm Regulations, and although a considerable area of land at a distance from the river has been improved by the works the expense is borne solely by the frontagers.

The Land Drainage Act, 1918, has now fortunately made it possible for the expenses incurred under such a scheme to be spread in future over all the lands benefited by the works.

By March, 1918, drainage work in the county had increased considerably, and it was found necessary to appoint a special Sub-Committee to deal with all matters relating to land drainage. It is interesting to note in view of the recent suggested delegation of powers by the Board of Agriculture to a Committee composed of eight members elected by the County Council and four by the Board of Agriculture after consultation with the County Executive Committees, that the Cambridgeshire Drainage Committee now consists of eleven members, six of whom are County Councillors. A full time Surveyor is employed working under the instructions of this Committee.

Early in 1918 at the request of a number of owners and occupiers the Committee took in hand the improvement of Isleham Fen, an area of about 3,500 acres with a variety of soils. There are about 100 occupiers of land within the area and a portion of the Fen is market garden land. The Fen lies at a height varying from 1 to 12 feet above sea level. Portions of the Fen have been lowered by paring and burning and by digging for fuel. The Board of Agriculture on the suggestion of the Committee issued an order in June last prohibiting the paring and burning of Fen land in the county of Cambridgeshire, except in cases where the permission of the Committee had been first obtained. A survey of the Fen was made and levels were taken. In March, 1918, a number of prisoners were allotted and commenced work under the instruction of working civilian foremen. The work is now, after eleven months, nearing completion. Some 11 miles of main drains with a top width varying from 9 to 14 feet have been opened out, deepened and widened, the sides given a correct batter, and the material removed thrown back from the drains. The prisoners are supplied with knee-boots for the work and the water in the drains is held up by dams which are drawn at night. No fewer than forty-eight gateway tunnels have been fixed in the drains; these are elm trunks of uniform size: no other form of tunnel has been found to be suitable in Fen land. A number of these tunnels are supplied with slats which fix into a frame in order to hold up water for stock in dry weather. The Fen is approached by a number of wide parallel Fen droves on either side of which are usually found the main drains. The droves are common for stock grazing and a number of drinking places have been made and fenced off from the drains.

For the drainage of the Fen it has been found necessary to open up an old catchwater drain on the edge of the Fen. In its course through a gravel hill the sides had slipped in and the drain was overgrown, and for many years the upland water had flowed into the Fen instead of being conveyed along its edge by the catchwater drain. Now that the old catchwater has been opened the Fen land will be relieved of this water, and only in times of drought will water be passed into the Fen from the catchwater.

There still remains an area of about 300 acres at the northern and lower end of the Fen to be dealt with. For the drainage of this area it will be necessary to erect a small pumping station to lift the water into the main drain which is carried across the area at high level and is ultimately raised into the River Lark by the pumping station at Prickwillow.

In addition to the operations carried out in Isleham Fen good work has been executed in the main drains through the low-lying country at Swavesey. Some work has also been carried out by prisoner labour in Waterbeach Fen. It is thought that, provided sufficient labour is found, an area of between 4,000 and 5,000 acres can be greatly improved in this district.

Several schemes are under consideration for the improvement of small areas including the drainage of Barway Fen, the reclamation of Chippenham Fen and the improvement of Wilbraham Fen.

The greatest task before the Committee is the clearing and opening up of the River Cam and its main tributaries, the Rivers Granta and Rhee, and the Bourn Brook. It is by the Cam and its tributaries that practically all the drainage water of Cambridgeshire is discharged. Their present condition is deplorable. A large number of trees have fallen from the banks and re-rooted. Shoals of mud have formed from the edges extending in many places practically across the river. A survey was made and from sections plotted from the levels taken it was shown that the average sectional area of accumulated mud was nearly three times that of the present sectional area available for water.

On the River Granta there are eleven mills on a course of about 17 miles, and as the fall is not great the mill leets in most cases are embanked and the water is conveyed to the mills at a higher level than the surrounding land. In many cases the millers who claim the water rights hold up the water but do not keep the river banks in repair. Owing to the large accumulation of mud in the channel and to the condition of the banks much water leaves the river, flowing over the surrounding land and filling up the smaller ditches and drains.

It is proposed that when the condition of the river has been improved, provision shall be made for the fixing of a tablet at each mill indicating the maximum head of water that shall be held, and that provision shall be made for each mill to be supplied with a spill-water or tumbling bay, and that each mill shall be provided with a sluice gate which shall be drawn up for a fixed number of hours at regular periods in order to encourage scour and to prevent the formation of shoals. It is suggested that some form of direct communication shall be fixed between all the mills so that one miller will be able to keep the miller below informed of the state of the water in times of flood.

If these upland waterways are to be improved it behoves the authorities responsible for the maintenance of the lower reaches of the Cam and Ouse to make adequate provision for the outfall of the upland water to the sea: otherwise, with the increased discharge in a shorter period, the banks on the lower reaches of the river which protect the Fen lands will be severely tested, and when it is considered that in addition to the work mentioned above the West Suffolk Committee is executing similar work on the River Lark, and the Bedfordshire Committee on the Ivel, the necessity of improving the lower course of the Ouse appears to be one of vital importance for the protection of the Fen farmer.

The Cambridgeshire Agricultural Executive Committee fully realizing the position of the Fen man invited the Executive Committees of Norfolk, West Suffolk, Isle of Ely, Huntingdonshire, and Bedfordshire to meet them and discuss the matter. A joint meeting of delegates was held at Cambridge on October 8th last. The outcome of this meeting has been that the Norfolk, Isle of Ely, Bedford, Huntingdon and Cambridge County Councils have petitioned the Board of Agriculture and Fisheries to form one joint authority for the administration of the Great Ouse and its tributaries. It is suggested that this authority, if set up, should be a governing body for the main river and should have power to exercise control when necessary over the forty-four drainage and embankment authorities now responsible for the water course.

INDEX

Index

Index